D1176612

be THIN through MOTIVATION

Published by:
Maurice Larocque Health Books
4335 Verdun Ave.
Verdun, Québec, Canada
H4G 1L6
Tel.: (514) 769-7822

Maurice
Larocque md

Translated by Robert E. Brewer

To my wife Jocelyne and my three children, Jean-François, Marie-Christine and Caroline, who have enabled me to put into practice in my daily life the wonderful techniques for happiness taught herein.

Maurice Larocque has been a medical doctor for fifteen years specializing in the psychology of the obese.

Frequently invited to speak before groups of physicians and other medical professionals, he is also a popular figure on radio, television and at public conferences in the United States and Canada as well as in Europe.

Other works by Dr. Larocque include: 2 series of 4 audio cassettes entitled *Be Thin By Suggestion* and *Be Thin, Be Motivated*; a video slim cassette program entitled *Are You A Winner Or A Loser?* and two computer programs *Bert* (a behavior monitor) and *Liza* (a program to help you identify motivational blocks). He is currently working on his latest book *Be Thin, Master Your Emotions, to be published shortly.*

Dr. Larocque is a member of the American Society of Bariatric Physicians (ASBP) and for the past 3 years has been President of A.M.T.O., its Canadian counterpart.

TABLE OF CONTENTS

The case histories presented in this book are true. Only the names have been changed in the interest of confidentiality.

THE END

Are you surprised to see "The End" right at the beginning of this volume? Well, it's because this book is unique — unlike any other book ever written on obesity.

This book will mark for you the end of negative thoughts which have prevented you from succeeding. It will mark the end of your disappointment, the end of your low self-esteem, the end of your lack of self-confidence, in short, the end of your dark days. Failure will be a thing of the past.

From the very first lines, this book will provide you with the means and motivation to succeed.

FOREWORD

This book will appeal to you because of its human qualities. Because the case histories presented herein are of people not unlike yourself, you'll be able to identify with them and gain valuable insights into your own problems. You'll also gain the motivation you need to succeed. If others have succeeded, why not you?

The vast amount of information contained in this book cannot be absorbed in one reading. Therefore, I suggest you read it rather quickly at first, and then go over it again slowly, while taking notes. You may wish to read several times those chapters and paragraphs that are of particular interest to you.

To be effective, *Be Thin Through Motivation* requires careful study. Why not make it your bedside book?

Maurice Larocque, M.D.

CHAPTER 1

KEYS TO SUCCESS

The evolution of science

Since the dawn of history, man's knowledge has increased dramatically. All the knowledge acquired from cave-dwelling days to 1750 had doubled by the year 1900. This means that it took only 150 years to increase twofold all the knowledge gained over the centuries. By 1950, just 50 years later, man's knowledge had again grown 100 percent, and from 1950 to 1965 it doubled once more, this time in 15 years. By 1975, a mere decade later, knowledge had doubled again, and it would do so once more by 1980.

The more science progresses, the more our knowledge grows. We're living in a period of adaptation to change, as our expanding knowledge changes the world around us — for better and for worse.

In a single day we receive more information than our grandparents did in an entire lifetime. This bombardment of information has an enormous impact on our lives. Although there is undoubtedly much more positive than negative in this avalanche of new data, it is up to the individual to be selective and to use this information wisely.

The aim of this book is to help you benefit from all the new possibilities offered by science, so that you may succeed in losing weight. If you really want to change, if you have the intense desire to lead a happy life — and I believe this to be the case because you're reading this book — the new insights we have gained into human physiology and behavior will enable you to attain your goal.

This book will be your guide. Written in a simple and clear manner, it presents techniques that have been thoroughly tested over the years and whose effectiveness is borne out by the many case histories described herein. If others have succeeded, why not you?

Illness: a choice

So far as obesity is concerned, man's knowledge has until now been a double-edged sword. It is alarming to note that, in all the so-called advanced industrial or post-industrial societies, we have created a host of affluence-related diseases. These diseases are responsible for 83 percent of all deaths before the age of 65. Although our knowledge in the fields of nutrition, physiology, and human behavior has never been greater, and although our impressive arsenal of new medicines and treatments is increasing day by day, from 1900 to 1970 man's life expectancy increased by only four years, from 63 to 67.

On the other hand, a few easily acquired habits such as enjoying a good breakfast, eating moderately, having three meals a day, exercising, not smoking, drinking little or no alcohol, and sleeping seven or eight hours a night,

Figure 1
LIFE EXPECTANCY

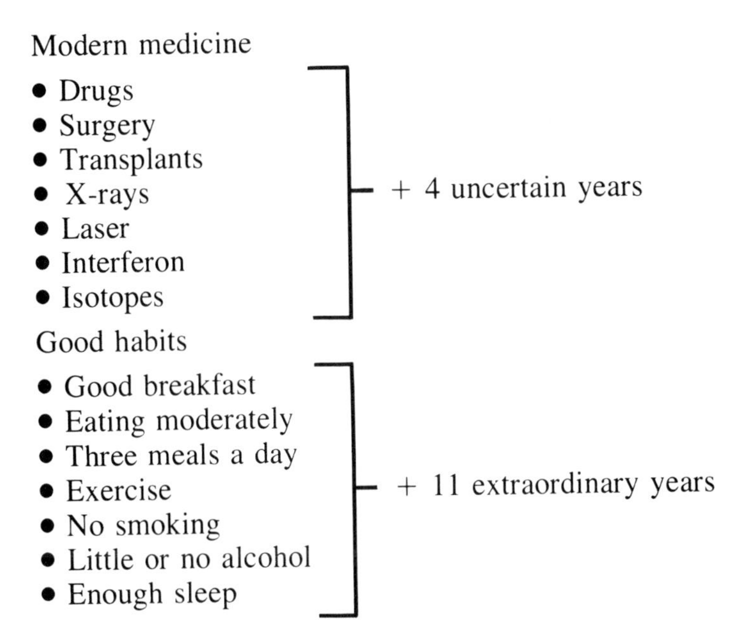

can increase our life expectancy by eleven years, from 67 to 78.

Dr. Kenneth Cooper, the father of jogging and author of the famous book *Aerobics,* written in 1968, states that a man of 45 can expect to live to 67 if he has less than four of the above habits; if he has four or five of these habits, he can expect to live to age 73; and, if he has six or seven, his life expectancy will be 78 years.

What we do for our bodies can prolong our life expectancy by eleven years, while vastly improving the quality of our lives. On the other hand, modern medical technology can extend our life expectancy by just four years, often delaying death by only a few, sometimes miserable, days.

In his Texas clinic, Dr. Cooper evaluated the physical fitness of persons aged 30 who jogged three times a week and maintained their ideal weight. He then compared them with 60-year-olds who followed the same training program and had the same lifestyle. The test used was an electrocardiograph connected to a treadmill. The results showed that it is possible at age 60 to be almost as physically fit as a 30-year-old.

Figure 2

PHYSICAL FITNESS

A fit 60-year-old	=	A fit 30-year-old

A sportsman

I am always amazed at certain patients who come into my office for their annual checkup. Tim, a successful businessman, has been coming to see me every year. Nothing can prevent him from keeping his appointment. He wants to undergo every possible test for cancer, diabetes, and cholesterol. As he puts it: "Health is precious. One shouldn't wait for one's health to fail to really appreciate it."

Tim is 36 years old and weighs 280 pounds. He smokes fifty cigarettes a day, skips meals, doesn't have breakfast, drinks alcohol every day, and sleeps an average of five hours a night because of his job. But he's an avid sportsman. During one consultation he told me about all the baseball games on TV and asked me if I occasionally went to the ball park. When I told him I didn't, he retorted, "Aren't you a sportsman, Doc?" I couldn't help smiling. A few months earlier I had participated in a ski marathon and had gone through five months of intensive training for the event. I still jog on a regular basis and also play tennis.

Tim followed all the sports at the stadium and on television but did not actively participate in any. A real sportsman!

One year, when Tim came for his yearly checkup, I diagnosed a serious case of diabetes. His sugar level while fasting was 342 (80 - 110 is normal). A year later, Tim's weight was the same and he hadn't changed his habits. Although I strongly advised him to lose his excess weight, he did nothing about it. A few months later, he lapsed into a diabetic coma and had to be hospitalized for three weeks. Today he still has the same weight problem and still suffers from diabetes. He believes in medical science but will do nothing to keep his body healthy.

In 1980, Americans spent $240 billion on health care, but only 3 percent of this total went towards prevention. Between 1968 and 1980, deaths from heart disease decreased by 23 percent. Why? Because of new methods of treatment? No. The reason is that Americans are taking better care of their bodies. Sixty percent of the population are now non-smokers. People are more concerned with nutrition, go for regular checkups, and exercise more. In 1968, the year *Aerobics* came out, there were less than 100,000 joggers; in 1980, there were 27 million. The 3 percent of $240 billion spent on prevention has done more to increase our life expectancy and to improve the quality of our lives than the other 97 percent.

CHAPTER 2

BRAINWASHING

A negative society

When you ask someone: "How are you?" the answer you most often hear is: "Not bad." The next time someone asks you this question, try this: give the person a big, honest-to-goodness smile and say: "Very well, thank you. I feel just wonderful today!" Watch his reaction. He'll become ill at ease, avoid looking you in the eye, and start fidgeting. He'll appear very unhappy to have bumped into you. You'll almost be able to read his mind: "This person's not normal. Who does he think he is? He must be crazy."

The news on the radio, on television, and in the newspapers is always bad: accidents, murders, unemployment, inflation and strikes. Even the weather forecast is lousy: there's a 20 percent chance of rain or thundershowers.

Positive and negative

Recently, during a workshop I was directing on behavior, motivation, and obesity, a participant made the following observation: "You know, Dr. Larocque, I've just learned that things can be positive or negative. I used to think everything was neutral, that things were simply the way they were, and that there was no way I could change anything, especially my attitudes." In her mind, if things were going badly, it was normal — there was nothing she could do about it; if things were going well, she was just lucky, and all she could do was enjoy her good fortune, nothing more. Her destiny was predetermined. She didn't know that she could react in different ways to a given situation. An optimist sees a glass as half full; a pessimist sees the same glass as half empty. My patient had been so conditioned by her surroundings, by television, and by society that she felt powerless to change anything or to make choices of her own free will. She simply accepted life as it was handed to her.

Lose, lose, lose . . .

A few years ago, Jessica, 54, came to my office. Barely 20 pounds overweight, she nevertheless seemed quite troubled by her excess pounds. She told me she'd been seeing a doctor regularly for almost 10 years for her weight problem, but with no success. If she lost one pound, she'd gain it back the following week. When I asked her what drugs had been prescribed for her, she hesitated, and then said she rarely took any. When I pressed the issue, however, she opened her purse and produced a list of the drugs she was taking.

Jessica's weight problem was making her a nervous wreck. The doctor who was treating her was very strict and would lecture her during her weekly consulation if she hadn't lost any weight since her previous visit. Actually,

Jessica felt she deserved to be admonished because she cheated. So, each week before her appointment, she would take a pill to eliminate water, a laxative and, if necessary, an enema, to be sure that she had eliminated everything and that she would weigh as little as possible when she stepped on the doctor's scales. She was very apprehensive about how her doctor would react, especially if she hadn't lost any weight during the week, so she began taking tranquilizers a couple of days before her appointments and a sleeping pill the night before. If her diet wasn't going well, she would become desperate and skip two or three meals in the hope of losing the necessary weight before her weekly visit. After the appointment, if her doctor was satisfied with her weight, she would sigh with relief and, famished from having skipped several meals, rush to the nearest restaurant. If the scales brought bad news, she would feel guilty and, in order to punish herself, head for the restaurant and pig out.

For years, Jessica and her doctor thought that to be slim and happy it was necessary to give up something. One had to give up one's favorite foods, eliminate certain habits, sacrifice evenings on the town, to lose pounds. But how could Jessica and her doctor expect to solve her weight problem if they concentrated only on the negative?

Applause

Marilyn's excess pounds equaled her age: 42. She didn't feel good about herself so she decided to do something about it and joined a weight-loss program. After a few weeks, despite having lost five pounds, she became increasingly sullen, impatient, and aggressive. "I feel I'm going crazy," she said to me. Separated from her husband, she had custody of her two daughters, aged 14 and 9. It was a big responsibility, and she had difficulty coping at times.

Marilyn was having a particularly rough week because of problems at work. When she came to her weekly weight-loss class, she hadn't lost a pound and was rather disappointed, especially since she'd handled the stress at her job better than usual and hadn't eaten as she used to in such situations. Sitting in the class, she heard one of her friends boast about how she'd cheated on her diet: "I had a piece of the most delicious pecan pie. The best I've ever eaten." A few moments later, the instructor called upon her friend and asked how she was progressing. Despite having cheated on her diet, she'd managed to lose weight. The class applauded. Then came Marilyn's turn; she hadn't lost an ounce. No applause. The group had just rewarded the one who had cheated and snubbed the one who had behaved well.

Marilyn felt guilty about her inability to lose weight. After all, the scales don't lie, or do they? Actually, the scales are the most negative element in a weight-reduction program. They make no distinction between loss of fat and fluctuations in body water. Water accounts for 60 percent of our total weight. Was it more important for Marilyn to lose one pound than to control her nerves? How can one solve a problem if one concentrates only on the negative?

The scales

Jan came to the clinic for her fourth visit. She looked radiant — in one month, she'd lost 16 pounds. When I met her in the waiting room, she mentioned how happy she was and how great she felt since she began losing weight. I told her I'd see her in a couple of minutes, after my assistant weighed her. Fifteen minutes later, Jan had yet to appear in my office, so I asked my secretary where she was. "Your patient seemed very happy up to the moment she stepped on the scales. Then, suddenly, she turned pale, burst into tears, and rushed out of the office.'' Jan had gained one pound.

Thus ended Jan's weight-loss program. Her sister, also a patient of mine, explained to me what had happened. Apparently, Jan hadn't been able to accept the idea that a small treat she'd indulged in had caused her to gain one pound. Feeling desperate and guilty, she considered the scales a penalty for having cheated on her diet. She fled the office, believing she no longer deserved the care of a doctor.

Jan lost a great opportunity to improve herself and to understand herself better. She chose to focus on the negative — the scales. She regarded the scales as a judge who had found her guilty and punished her. How can one solve a problem if one concentrates only on the negative?

The people around us

''My God, you look old. You've lost too much weight. Stop your ridiculous diet right now — you look miserable. Here, I just baked your favorite chocolate cake. It's scrumptious. Aren't you sick of depriving yourself? You only have one life to live. I, for one, would rather be fat and happy and eat whatever I want. You don't know what you're missing.'' A person on a diet will frequently hear such words from a plump friend and, unfortunately, even the most steadfast dieter will often be swayed by such talk. Some people are very negative and try by the most ingenious means to discourage someone who is striving to reach his or her goal. On the other hand, it is not unusual to hear these same people say: ''Look at her. Is she ever fat! She shouldn't dress like that — she's making a spectacle of herself. Well, she has only herself to blame. Just look at her eat.''

It's very important to understand the negative influence of the people around us. We shall now examine three of the major reasons why some people act the way they do.

Ignorance

Jim was quite fond of Cathy. She was very unhappy, though, because she was 88 pounds overweight. Two years previous she had lost 77 pounds and felt marvelous. However, the death of her mother, problems at work, and a new nursing job had caused her to neglect her eating habits and she gradually gained back all her weight.

I met Cathy again by chance at a social gathering. She was pleased to see me but felt embarrassed and guilty for having gained back her weight. For several weeks she'd thought about coming to see me again, but her pride had prevented her from doing so. I reassured her and urged her to resume her weight-reduction program.

Cathy's friend, Jim, was at her side during our conversation. He was lean despite being a hearty eater and a heavy drinker. "You'll never make it, Cathy," he said. "It's always the same story — you lose weight and then you gain it back. You're a hopeless case."

Jim's remarks were a blow to Cathy's ego and made her lose all her self-confidence and hope of success. It was too bad. Just because one has failed in the past doesn't mean one will always fail. If one can learn from one's mistakes, the possibility of succeeding the next time will be that much greater. Walt Disney went bankrupt seven times before succeeding. Had he given up after the first attempt, or after the second or third, had he not learned from his errors to increase his chances of success, his Wonderful World would never have materialized.

Jim loved Cathy. Deep inside, he really wanted her to lose weight, but he didn't know how to help her.

Whenever she began a new diet, he was the first one to offer her a treat: "C'mon, you've had a good week. You've lost a few pounds — let's celebrate. I know a great Italian restaurant. You'll go back on your diet Monday."

Jim enjoyed going to restaurants but didn't like to go alone. He was willing for Cathy to lose her extra pounds as long as it didn't interfere with his lifestyle. Since he had no trouble maintaining his weight without depriving himself, why could't she? Jim loved Cathy very much but understood nothing about the problem of obesity and even less about psychology.

Loss of domination

Diane was a young patient of 24 who had been married for two years. She was 5 feet 2 inches tall and weighed 175 pounds. When I first saw her, she seemed to understand her problem and agreed to go on a diet to lose her excess weight and to follow my behavior modification program. She said she could finally see the light at the end of the tunnel. "I'm going to be beautiful both inside and out," she beamed.

After losing 15 pounds in one month, Diane failed to show up for her fifth appointment. When my secretary contacted her to confirm her next visit, Diane told her she'd quit her diet and her bahavior program, but gave no explanation. It was bewildering to see a woman who had shown so much enthusiasm and obtained such good results give up so suddenly. Diane's mother, whom I was treating for a minor weight problem, telephoned my office to apologize for her daughter: "Diane has been married for two years to a very jealous man. Before her marriage, she was only a few pounds overweight, but her husband is a bad influence on her. He does everything he can to make her gain weight. He buys her sundaes, pies, chips, and soft drinks. When he learned that Diane was following your diet, he threatened her and forbade her ever to see you again. My daughter can't stand up for herself and is afraid of her husband, so she obeys him." Here is a case of a woman dominated by her husband who had no fear of losing her as long as she remained fat.

Often, it is a friend of the same sex who acts as a negative influence on a dieter. I recall a patient of mine who couldn't understand the behaviour of her friend at work, a woman with whom she'd been close for years.

My patient was 44 pounds overweight; her friend was very slim. In the office where they worked together as secretaries for four bosses, they were the only women. When my patient began her weight-loss program, everything went well. Then, suddenly, her friend began criticizing her diet; she said it didn't suit her, that she'd aged considerably, and that she was making herself ill. My patient was shaken; she didn't know what to think. Perhaps her friend was right. Then came invitations from her friend to dine out and, finally, a party at her friend's home. It was a real feast: champagne, hors d'oeuvres, roast beef, chicken, pasta, and every dessert imaginable, from French pastries to Black Forest cake. Her friend insisted that she try everything: "I prepared this dish especially for you," she said. "You'll just love it."

My patient was flabbergasted. Why the sudden attention? Why so many temptations? What happened was that when my patient started to lose weight, her employers began paying her compliments and showing her more attention, attention that her friend had been used to receiving. Her friend suddenly felt less attractive; she had a competitor and wanted to eliminate her.

When a person loses weight, a friend may fear that their relationship will change or that their friendship will fall apart. Often, it's a case of losing power over someone who has become more attractive and confident.

Guilt

Ann and Jennifer were sisters-in-law and got along very well. Both were about 40 pounds overweight. When they went to a social gathering they were the life of the party, laughing and singing and telling jokes. They almost gave the impression that fat is fun.

One day, Ann decided that she'd had it with her weight problem and vowed to get rid of her excess pounds once and for all. She confessed to me: "I'm sick and tired of clowning around all the time and pretending to be happy when I'm not. When you're fat, people think you're supposed to be jolly. You can never look sad, not even for a single day."

Most people appreciate something only when they no longer have it. Ann wanted badly to get back her looks, her youth, and her self-esteem, so she embarked on her new diet with enthusiasm and determination.

When Jennifer learned that Ann was going on a diet, she too decided to lose some weight. If her sister-in-law could do it, why couldn't she? After all, it wouldn't do her any harm. Within seven weeks, Jennifer lost 11 pounds. Although she felt better, the thought of depriving herself any longer was too much for her, so she dropped her diet. Ann stuck it out. She had suffered so much with her weight problem that what she gained each day in well-being and self-esteem more than made up for any dishes she had to give up.

After a few weeks, the relationship between the two sisters-in-law grew tense. Jennifer became increasingly hostile: "Ever since you started that infernal diet, you've been impossible to get along with. Why don't you just give it up?" At first, Ann was hurt by Jennifer's comments and was afraid of losing her as a friend. How was it that someone who was supposed to care for her was doing everything she could to see her fail? "If she were a true friend," she thought, "she'd help me instead of hurting me."

I'm sure Jennifer liked Ann. The problem was that her guilt feelings aroused by Ann's success were greater than her feelings of affection. Jennifer probably thought: "How come Ann can solve her weight problem and I can't? After all, she's no better than I am." The truth is, though, that Jennifer felt inferior to Ann and found her success hard to accept. If Ann failed, she would certainly feel a bit sad for her, but at least she wouldn't feel inferior.

It was important for Ann to realize that Jennifer was the truly unhappy one, and that she would do anything in her power to get rid of her feelings of failure and guilt.

CHAPTER 3

THE ILLUSION OF HAPPINESS

At last, something positive

We live in a negative society in which we're continually bombarded with bad news. Negative influences abound. What we require is something positive, something upbeat. In our society, it is advertising that provides us with this much-needed dose of optimism.

While watching television, we often witness scenes of terrible violence and brutality. However, every ten minutes or so we're transported from the world of murders, rapes, and kidnappings into an entirely different setting. Suddenly, we're watching a happy family enjoying a chicken dinner, or viewing gorgeous girls in bikinis prancing on the beach. What a relief! It's good to escape into a dreamworld filled with beautiful people and happy families, to see something positive for a change. I, for one, would much rather go sailing or camping with my family than watch someone get murdered.

Advertisements in newspapers, on television, and on the radio are an island of hope in a sea of negativism. Advertisers are fully aware of this situation and exploit it to the fullest.

From positive to negative

I often hear people say: ''Advertisements don't influence me. I buy only what I really need. They can run their ads for fast food as often as they like — I never touch the stuff.''

Okay, so you don't like hamburgers, and all the advertisements in the world can't induce you to eat them. However, even if you don't buy the advertised item, you are buying the idea (and this is even worse) that in order to be happy, it is necessary to buy, to eat, to consume something.

Everyone wants to be happy — it's only normal. Advertisers sell us the idea that we can attain happiness by purchasing something, and they bombard us with this message day after day. Advertising wakes us associate an advertised product with happiness, so much so that we become unhappy and feel as if we're missing out on something if we can't obtain such and such a product.

Whether it be lack of money that is preventing you from purchasing a particular item, or your health (or perhaps a diet) that is stopping you from eating a certain food, you end up feeling that something is lacking in your life, something without which you cannot be happy. You believe you have as much right to happiness as everyone else, so you feel deprived.

Whenever I watch beer commercials featuring sports and athletes, I always wonder how they affect an obese person who is on a diet. Is the dieter more frustrated at not being able to drink beer, or at not being able to play basketball, tennis, or volleyball?

While I believe that advertising is necessary to our type of society, those who view ads should see them for what they are and take them with a grain of salt.

The athlete you see in an ad is happy because of his performance; he's proud of his exploits, which are more important than any beer he may drink, The bikini-clad girl on the beach is happy because people find her attractive; she feels good about herself, which is of greater importance than the brand of soft drink she prefers. The family in the restaurant is happy not because of the food they're eating, but because they're together, enjoying each other's company.

It would be great if beer ads induced people to participate in sports, if food ads prompted people to keep themselves trim, and if restaurant ads made people want to spend more time with family and friends. Unfortunately, such is not the case. Each commercial must be viewed objectively, its message analyzed in a realistic way. Since advertisements provide us with much-needed positive images in a world dominated by negativity, it's easy to be seduced by the scenes of happiness they depict. Stop for a moment and ask yourself if you can really buy happiness.

I'm not saying that we can't derive pleasure from owning a product or eating a food whose praises are sung in the media. The point I'm trying to make is that pleasure can't be equated with happiness. True happiness must be cultivated within us; pleasure is but the icing on the cake.

A myth

Look closely at the personalities featured in commercials. They are young, vibrant, beautiful, slim and sexy. They exude the happiness for which we yearn. Their message: "If you want to be happy like I am, do as I do. Eat, drink, use, buy my product." Obedient souls that we are, we rush out to the store and gorge ourselves on the goodies promoted on T.V. in the hope of attaining instant happiness. The results are staggering: 50 percent of the American population has a weight problem. One out of two people.

I'm sure that, in the other 50 percent of the population, not everyone eats as he should. Over the years, we end up paying for our poor dietary habits. The majority of Americans, between 75 and 80 percent, suffer from illnesses caused by improper nutrition. Have these people attained the happiness promised in advertisements?

Of the thousands of patients I see, most come to me with one of the following complaints: "I don't feel good about myself." "I don't like the way I look." "I hate myself." "I don't like to go out with my husband." "I'm ashamed of myself." "I feel like everyone's against me." "I no longer do any sports." "I can't wear bathing suits or shorts anymore." "I'm always tired and out of breath." "I have trouble bending over to tie my shoelaces." I have purposely omitted several highly derogatory remarks made by some of my patients when they look at themselves in the mirror.

For people who are easily swayed, advertisements can produce a feeling of frustration if they are unable to solve their weight problem. Our consumer society uses a subtle form of brainwashing — advertising — to create the illusion that happiness can be bought. Unfortunately, it has created something else in the process: a social catastrophe. I am referring to the epidemic of obesity that is sweeping the land and causing people so much unhappiness. And, ironically, our society is highly critical of obese people, the victims of its brainwashing.

"Have you ever seen anyone so fat? What a sight! It's her own fault — just look at her eat." "Look at that fat lady standing in line at the ice cream parlor. She can probably keep them in business all by herself." "If she's suffering from diabetes today, she has only herself to blame." "He died of a heart attack, but did you see how much weight he was carrying around? He was asking for it." "Look at how she's dressed. If I were that fat, I certainly wouldn't wear clothes like that." "If she gets on this plane, we'll never be able to get off the ground." While society has made obese people the butt of cruel jokes and biting sarcasm, it also feels pity for them: "Poor soul, she looks so pathetic." "He must have something wrong with his glands." "It really hurts me to see her that way."

All of us, regardless of whether we're fat or thin, are to blame for the obesity problem in our country. At the same time, we are also the victims. We believe we must eat to be happy, but that obese people have no right to happiness.

A society is made up of individuals, and what a society believes is a reflection of what the majority believes. Each individual, therefore, plays a crucial role. Are you negative toward others and yourself? Do you always notice your faults and those of others before you notice the good qualities? Do you always find good excuses to justify your behavior? Are you quick to blame others for your problems?

As an individual, you are part of both the problem and the solution.

True happiness

Through advertising, society has created the myth that we can buy happiness. According to this myth, happiness comes from outside the individual. In reality, however, things are quite different: true happiness can come only from within.

A few years ago, I was consulted by a young woman of 27 who was 45 pounds overweight. Employed as a journalist in the field of the arts, Jane led an active social life and boasted an impressive circle of friends and acquaintances. Her life was a continuous swirl of press conferences, restaurants, nightclubs, shows, and parties which often lasted till 3 or 4 in the morning. She had gained her 45 extra pounds in the three years since she began working as a journalist.

Jane confessed to me that life in the fast lane had left her a bit jaded. The first two years had been enjoyable and challenging, but now she felt as if she were just going through the motions. Driving a Corvette, traveling abroad, and dining at the finest restaurants had brought her pleasure, but not happiness. Despite her active social life, she felt lonely. Her life had no meaning.

Jane had been married for two years. Her husband of 41 had adapted well to her busy schedule and often accompanied her to social functions. They had agreed before their marriage not to have children. Although she came from a family of seven children and had truly enjoyed her years at home, she didn't want to have children herself because nowadays it was too great a responsibility. She knew many divorced couples whose children suffered as a result of their parents' separation. The high cost of educating children and the uncertain economic times were other reasons for not starting a family. She loved children too much to risk seeing them suffer. "In any event," she concluded, "my husband is too old."

Jane's explanations were long and arduous, as if she were trying to convince herself. During the whole time she was pleading her case, I didn't say a word. She would raise objections herself, and then proceed to answer them. At the end, I smiled at her. She stared back, a vacant look in her eyes. Half jokingly, I said to her: "I bet you five dollars you'll be pregnant within a year." "I'll take your bet," she replied. "I never wanted children, and I don't see why I should change my mind now."

Jane shed her excess weight with ease, dropping 28 pounds in two months. With a gleam in her eye, she handed me a five dollar bill. "I'm going to lose another 15 pounds and then I want to get pregnant," she said. "You've won your bet." Jane had found the goal she needed to be happy; she had discovered it within herself. She would take up the challenge and live her life as a woman to the fullest.

A year later, Jane gave birth to a beautiful girl who bore a remarkable resemblance to her mother — they were like two peas in a pod. When I met Jane and her husband at a party a few months later, she told me they were planning another child. This time, they wanted to have a boy and would call him Jason. It was good to see such a happy couple.

Jane's story illustrates that happiness can come only from within. Having children may not be the answer in your particular case and I'm certainly not suggesting that all women start a family. What I do suggest is that you look within yourself for the goals that are meaningful to you, and then strive to attain these goals. People are happy when they feel they are giving their utmost, when they push themselves to the limit and realize their full potential. People need challenges.

When you watch thousands of people running in a marathon, you can see the suffering etched on the faces of the participants as well as the satisfaction they feel upon finishing the race. A marathon is made up of housewives and businessmen, students and laborers, handicapped people in wheelchairs-thousands of ordinary people between the ages of 16 and 65, from all walks of life, experiencing happiness as they overcome the pain and exhaustion of their grueling run. We are all running in a marathon — the marathon of life. It is in overcoming life's difficulties that we attain true happiness.

CHAPTER 4

THE ART OF KILLING YOURSELF

Results

"We only have one life to live, so we might as well enjoy it. Anyway, we all have to die from something or other." This type of opinion, which I still hear quite often, seems to be the rallying cry of our society. We're becoming experts in the art of killing ourselves — the sooner we end our lives, the better.

Let's take a look at the leading causes of death in the United States.

1- *Cardiovascular disease* is the number one killer, causing approximately 38 percent of all deaths.

Factors contributing to cardiovascular disease are obesity, lack of exercise, stress, high blood pressure, diabetes, high blood cholesterol, and smoking. Although deaths due to heart disease have decreased 20 percent over the last ten years, people are now getting heart disease at a much younger age. Every week I see patients under 40 suffer heart attacks, most recently, a 32-year-old man. Married for five years and the father of two young children, the victim had an obesity problem and was also a smoker. What's more, he was suffering from stress and led a sedentary life. In order to improve his blood circulation, doctors had to perform bypass surgery.

2- *Cancer* is the second most deadly disease, accounting for about 21 percent of all deaths.

In males, lung cancer is the biggest killer, claiming three times as many lives as any other type of cancer. In the United States, the lung cancer mortality rate jumped from 4.6 per 100,000 males in 1932 to 76.4 per 100,000 males in 1975.

In women, it is breast cancer and lung cancer that are the most deadly, with each accounting for about 20 percent of all cancer deaths in 1980. Deaths from lung cancer are on the upswing, however, having risen from 2.5 per 100,000 females in 1932 to 16.6 in 1975. It won't be long before lung cancer passes breast cancer as the leading cause of cancer death in women.

The mortality rate for all other types of cancer, among both men and women, dropped considerably from 1932 to 1975, prompting cancer researchers to say that if it weren't for lung cancer they'd be on the way to licking the disease.

The primary cause of lung cancer is smoking. A smoker who goes through two packs a day increases his risk of getting lung cancer 25 times. Smoking one pack a day decreases one's life expectancy by 5.5 minutes a day, or 28 days a year.

It takes 20 years for tobacco's cancer-producing effects to be felt. Once cancer is diagnosed, it has usually already spread throughout the body so that the chances of surviving more than five years is only 30 percent.

3- *Cerebrovascular diseases,* which often result in strokes, claim the lives of some 200,000 Americans each year.

One of the major causes of cerebrovascular diseases is high blood pressure brought on by obesity and excessive salt consumption. The normal daily requirement of salt is two grams; most people eat 20 grams a day, 10 times the recommended amount.

4- *Accidents* claim the lives of over 100,000 Americans each year. Alcohol is involved in over 50 percent of all road fatalities.

5- *Cirrhosis of the liver* is claiming more and more lives each year. The main cause of this deadly disease: alcohol. In the United States there are approximately 30 million alcoholics, including 3 million adolescents. Deaths due to alcohol are growing at a faster rate than deaths from any other cause.

Diet and breast cancer

The number one cause of death among women aged 35 to 54 is breast cancer. According to several medical reports published in the last few years, there is a higher incidence of breast cancer in obese women than in thin women. These findings suggest a link between excessive consumption of certain foods and the formation or development of the disease. While I do not claim to have found the causes of breast cancer — they are still unknown — there are certain facts which cannot be ignored.

Although it is still not known how dietary fat affects the formation and development of certain cancers, research by Dr. K. Carroll of Western University in London, Ontario and by Dr. P.B. Mc Kay of the Oklahoma Medical Research Foundation in Oklahoma City has shown that the incidence of breast cancer increases with the amount of fat eaten.

A study published in November 1979 at Ohio State Medical School provides us with some interesting data. Forty-seven patients with multiple cysts in the breasts were divided into two groups. Twenty-seven were put on a special diet as the only form of treatment; the remaining twenty served as the control group and received neither special diet nor treatment.

After six months, the two groups were reevaluated. There was no imporvement in the condition of the control group; however, of the group following the special diet, 65 percent had gone into complete remission — they no longer had any cysts.

The diet of these patients was simple: no coffee, no tea, no cola and no chocolate. Methyl-xanthine, a chemical found in these products, is an apparent cause of multiple cysts in the breast.

We are indeed becoming experts at the art of killing ourselves. We don't die from diseases; rather, we die from what we do to our bodies during our lifetime.

The role of obesity

Obesity, because of the role it plays in heart disease, high blood pressure, diabetes, and the level of cholesterol and fat in the blood, is responsible for more deaths than cancer.

If a miracle drug were invented that could totally wipe out cancer, our life expectancy would increase by two years; but, if we could eliminate obesity overnight, our life expectancy would be prolonged by seven years.

According to a study performed by Dr. Drennick on 200 obese males who were at least 30 percent above their ideal weight, the risk of death for an overweight male between age 25 and 34 is twelve times greater than normal;

between 35 and 44, it is six times greater; between 45 and 54, three times greater.

A 14-year study of various death-risk factors, conducted in Framingham, Massachusetts, found that a 10 percent weight increase carried an added death risk of 30 percent; when the weight increase was between 30 and 50 percent, the death risk jumped 54 percent; for a weight increase of between 50 and 74 percent, the risk of death soared 130 to 182 percent. The fatter you are, the slimmer your chances of living long.

A 50-year-old man who is 44 pounds overweight can expect to live another 18 years, to age 68. However, a man of the same age who is at his ideal weight will probably live another 25 years, to age 75. In other words, 44 pounds of excess weight will cost a 50-year-old man seven years of life.

Diabetes

There are 12 million diabetics in the United States. Insurance companies regularly study life-threatening diseases and base their premiums on the degree of risk these diseases carry. Actuaries hired by these firms have published the following findings: if you are 20 percent over your ideal weight, your chances of premature death from diabetes are 150 percent above normal; if your are carrying 30 percent too much weight, your risk of dying prematurely is 400 percent higher.

The consequences of diabetes are devestating: heart attacks, paralysis, blindness, amputation, and coma. Nevertheless, 80 percent of diabetics could keep their disease under control without medication if they could get down to their ideal weight and maintain it. In fact, 80 percent of diabetics wouldn't be diabetics if they weren't obese. Poor nutrition is responsible for 80 percent of all diabetes cases.

High blood pressure

High blood pressure has often been called the silent killer because the vast majority of those affected by the disease have no symptoms. Half of its victims know nothing about their illness since they've never had their blood pressure checked. An estimated 40 million Americans suffer from high blood pressure, about one out of six people. Because most are unaware they have the disease, they don't seek medical treatment. Of those receiving treatment, only half are able to control their blood pressure adequately. The longterm consequences of high blood pressure are deadly. For 10 or 20 years there are no symptoms — then suddenly it hits: poor blood circulation in the legs, paralysis and heart attacks. It's too late then — the damage has been done.

There are two known causes of high blood pressure: salt and obesity. Excessive salt consumption, up to 10 times the required amount, is very harmful. If you think you may be adding too much salt to your food and are trying to do something about it, check for sodium chloride — another name for salt — on the labels of the food products you buy. You may be surprised to learn that prepared foods contribute up to two thirds of your salt intake.

Obesity plays an even greater role than salt in the development of high blood pressure. Almost half of those suffering from the disease could reduce their blood pressure by simply controlling their weight. That's right — one out of two persons with high blood pressure could cure his condition without medication by merely maintaining his ideal weight.

Be good to your body

The human body is a marvelous machine. It has the power to take you to the highest heights. However, as soon as you mistreat your body — even the slightest bit — you're asking for trouble.

Your body wasn't designed to be obese; if you insist on making it so, you must pay the price — and it is a high price.

You die from what you do to your body during your lifetime. Medical science does not have the answer — it can prolong your life by only a few miserable hours. Take responsibility for your body and get the most out of your life.

CHAPTER 5

DEATH IN YOUR PLATE

The food we eat

The number one cause of obesity is the food we eat. Over the last few decades, we have witnessed an unprecedented epidemic of obesity: one American out of two now has a weight problem.

In 1977, a Senate commission headed by George McGovern examined the dietary habits of Americans and established certain nutritional guidelines.

Foods fall into three categories: proteins, fats, and carbohydrates.

Glucides — commonly known as carbohydrates, or sugars — account for 46 percent of our daily caloric intake; 24 percent of our calories are in the form of refined sugars and 22 percent in the form of complex sugars, or starches. The nutritional guidelines recommend that we increase our glucide consumption to 58 percent of our daily caloric intake by raising our consumption of starches, which are absorbed slowly, to 45 percent and by lowering our consumption of refined sugar to 13 percent.

Fat represents 42 percent of our caloric intake: 16 percent in the form of saturated fats of animal origin and 26 percent in the form of unsaturated fats of vegetable origin. According to the nutritional guidelines, we should decrease the amount of fat we eat to 30 percent of our caloric intake, with animal fats comprising 10 percent and vegetable fats 20 percent.

Proteins make up 12 percent of our diet. While this percentage is considered satisfactory, it is suggested that we eat less red meat and more fish, chicken, eggs, and dairy products.

Our total daily caloric intake should be decreased from 3,000 to 2,000.

Glucides, the body's principal sources of energy, are of two types: slow-absorption and fast-absorption. Absorbed in the digestive tract over the course of several hours, slow-absorption sugars are composed primarily of starch. They are found in such foods as wheat, corn, rice, pasta, cereals, and potatoes. Fast absorption sugars are either simple or double; their absorption time is 18 to 20 minutes.

Simple sugars
- glucose (refined sugar)
- fructose (sugar from fruits, vegetables, honey)

Double sugars
- sucrose (cane sugar, beet sugar)
- lactose (milk sugar)
- maltose (malt sugar, from starch)

Refined sugar is a man-made product. It is one of the only foods that is absorbed into the blood stream in a chemically pure form requiring no conversion. The total absorption time is 18 - 20 minutes. As far as we know, the

Figure 3
DIETARY PATTERN

	Current Percentage of Total Caloric Intake		Recommended	
GLUCIDES (carbohydrates/ sugars)	Refined sugar	24%	Refined sugar	↓ 13%
	Starch	22%	Starch	↑ 45%
	TOTAL	46%	TOTAL	↑ 58%
FAT	Animal	16%	Animal	↓ 10%
	Vegetable	26%	Vegetable	↓ 20%
	TOTAL	42%	TOTAL	↓ 30%
PROTEINS	Meat	8%	Meat	↓ 4%
	Fish		Fish	
	Chicken	4%	Chicken	↑ 8%
	Other		Other	
	TOTAL	12%	TOTAL	12%
Calories per day:	3,000		↓ 2,000	

body can take up to 1.3 ounces of refined sugar per day without suffering any ill effects. In the United States, we consume 6.5 ounces daily, five times the safe limit. The worst part of it is that we're not always aware of how much sugar we're eating. The substance is found in countless food products such as canned goods, soft drinks, fruit drinks, yogurt, ice cream, cakes, jams, cookies, cereals, and even pickles. The next time you do your grocery shopping, check the labels and look for ingredients such as glucose, sucrose, saccharose and glucides — they all mean sugar.

A normal diet includes enough sugar for our needs; it's not necessary to add any sugar to our diet. Sugar is found in bread, pasta, fruits, peas, carrots, and milk. In fact, almost all foods contain sugar. I often hear patients say: "Doctor, I absolutely need sugar. When my body doesn't have enough, I feel sick." The fact is, nobody who enjoys a normal, well-balanced diet and who eats at regular intervals without skipping meals needs to add refined sugar to his diet. People crave sugar not because their body requires it, but because they like the taste and because eating generous amounts of sugar has become a habit. Some people will even tell you that sugar is their only joy in life and that their life wouldn't be worth living without sugar.

Bread and sugar

Why is refined sugar so harmful to our health? To answer this question, we shall first look at what happens inside our body when we eat a slice of 100% whole wheat bread, and what happens when we eat sugar.

Bread is a complex sugar composed of long chains, which are broken down by digestive enzymes to produce glucose, a simple natural sugar. This digestive process is slow and allows the sugar to be released into the blood stream gradually, over the course of one to three hours. The absorption of sugar into the blood stream stimulates the pancreas into producing insulin, which enables the body to use this sugar — from the liver to the cells. If the sugar is absorbed slowly, as when bread is eaten, the insulin will be produced over a longer period and in moderation.

On the other hand, when refined sugar is eaten, it is absorbed into the blood stream quickly, within 18 to 20 minutes. This rapid absorption of sugar overstimulates the pancreas, which then produces more insulin than is actually needed. The sugar is quickly stored and burned, but the excess insulin in the blood stream causes the blood-sugar level to drop well below normal. This condition is called hypoglycemia.

A vicious circle then begins. Hypoglycemia produces fatigue, impatience, aggressivity, loss of concentration, and, above all, ravenous hunger. The result is that a person suffering from hypoglycemia will again gorge himself with too much sugar because his stomach feels like a bottomless pit. Although the sweets bring temporary relief, they cause the insulin level in the blood to shoot up once more, thus provoking another attack of hypoglycemia three to five hours later.

Consequences

A direct consequence of the abuse of refined sugar is diabetes. Because the pancreas produces too much insulin and is overworked, it grows weaker and weaker until it can no longer metabolize the absorbed sugar, which then remains in the blood stream. The result is diabetes, with its host of complications.

Another consequence of eating too much refined sugar is obesity. It is estimated that the average person consumes 130 pounds of refined sugar a year; this sugar is transformed into 66 pounds of excess fat. The refining of sugars and starches, especially wheat and rice, plays a major role in the high incidence of obesity, diabetes, and intestinal cancer. Because refined wheat and rice are stripped of their dietary fiber, which contains no absorbable calories, the calories in the remaining part of the grain become concentrated in a relatively small volume. Consequently, when this grain is eaten, the stomach registers only a small quantity of food and keeps asking for more even though the caloric content of the food it already holds is very high.

In treating diabetes, it is now current practice to prescribe a diet rich in complex sugars, that is to say, unrefined starches. Preliminary results have shown such a diet to be effective in lowering appreciably the level of sugar in the blood. Studies by Dr. P. Burkitt of England have demonstrated the importance of a high-fiber diet in decreasing the risk of certain diseases. In countries whose inhabitants eat a great deal of fiber, constipation, diseases of the colon, and intestinal cancer are almost unheard of. In these countries, food remains in the intestines for about 35 hours, roughly a day and a half; in our society, it remains for 80 hours, about three and a half days.

Empty calories

Refined sugar provides empty calories, that is to say, it is a source of pure energy — calories — but contains no proteins, vitamins, or minerals. Since over one quarter of our daily diet is composed of these empty calories, we often lack the vitamins and minerals necessary for good health.

With sugar, man has refined the art of killing himself.

Meat

Meat is composed of two elements that provide energy: fat and protein.

Fats fall into two categories:

1- saturated fats, primarily of animal origin

2- unsaturated fats, primarily of vegetable and fish origin

Numerous studies are currently underway to evaluate the importance of unsaturated fats — certain margarines, for example — in reducing the blood cholestero level and, consequently, arteriosclerosis. The question is a complex one, and there is not yet any conclusive evidence that margarine is healthier than butter, or vice versa. While I do not know which side is right in the margarine-butter debate, I do know that we eat too many fatty foods. Fats presently account for 42 percent of our diet, whereas they should account for no more than 30 percent. We must therefore reduce our consumption of fats by over one quarter. It should be remembered that fats contain twice as many calories per ounce as sugars or proteins: fats burned in the body yield 255 calories per ounce, sugars or proteins, 113 calories.

Hidden fats

A sedentary woman who weighs 165 pounds eats 2,000 calories a day on the average. Of these calories, 850 are in the form of fats, the equivalent of 23.5 teaspoons of butter. I can already hear your reaction: "C'mon, I've never eaten that much butter in a single day — it's not possible." It is. In our society we usually eat meat twice a day. A meal without meat is not a meal. The fat content of a piece of uncooked meat with its water removed can be as high as 80 percent. Some examples:

— medium quality ground beef: 80% fat
— ham and pork: approximately 70% fat
— veal: approximately 55% fat
— chicken: approximately 40% fat
— sole: approximately 20% fat

All red meats contain more fat than protein. Only poultry and fish have a higher percentage of protein than fat. While a seven-ounce grilled steak contains almost 160 calories of protein, its fat content is over 450 calories, the equivalent of 13 teaspoons of butter. I hope you don't add any butter when cooking your steak.

Too much meat, and I believe twice a day is too much, is harmful to our health because of meat's high fat content. We would be much better off decreasing our meat consumption, which has doubled over the last 30 years, and increasing the amount of chicken, fish, and legumes we eat.

The joy of living

We are what we eat. Now, more than ever, it is important to eat well and choose the proper foods. Our industrialized society has made available to us a dazzling array of prepackaged, processed foods which are pleasing to the eye but often harmful to our health. Modern technology has broadened our horizons and opened up to us more possibilities than we've ever had before. Unfortunately, instead of getting the most out of life, we seem intent on shortening it. The pleasures we get out of life are small, the pains great.

It's up to you. You can either throw away your health, or enjoy a long, happy life. If you have decided upon the latter course, the nutrition guide below will get you off to a good start:

Figure 4

NUTRITION GUIDE

	Reduce by:
• salt	80 - 90%
• refined sugar	50 - 80%
• animal fat	50%
• calories	33%
	Increase by:
• unrefined starches	100%
• vegetable fat	(no change)
• fish	100%
• chicken	100%
• vegetables	100%

Just as your car requires the right gasoline to run smoothly, your body needs the proper foods to function as it should. Stuffing your body with sugar, salt, fat, and other harmful substances is like filling your automobile tank with sand and tar. Deadly.

CHAPTER 6

THE TREATMENT OF FAT

Crutches

People will probably always seek easy solutions to their weight problems. Appetite suppressants containing amphetamines were quite the rage a while back, although many have since been banned. If you took such pills, you probably recall feeling "pepped up" all the time and spending many a sleepless night.

Nowadays, appetite suppressants are almost all distant derivatives of amphetamines, but with far fewer side-effects. Although they are effective in promoting weight loss during the first six weeks, they seem to lose their effectiveness thereafter. A miracle pill has yet to be invented.

The water pill

Patients often ask me for water pills to help them lose weight. Unfortunately, such pills are totally useless for they don't eliminate fat. What's more, they can be dangerous since they dehydrate the body and the skin. Water pills should be used only for certain diseases, and then, only if prescribed by a doctor.

Thyroid gland extracts

Thyroid gland extracts are not very effective and can be harmful, especially if they cause heart palpitations. They have not been approved for the treatment of obesity.

Daily injections of Gonadotrophin Chorionic Hormone (G.C.H.)

Used primarily in conjunction with 500-calorie diets, G.C.H. injections have stirred considerable debate. Four recent studies conducted concurrently in the United States all showed no significant difference in either weight loss or well-being between groups receiving injections of G.C.H. (hormones produced by pregnant women) and placebo groups who believed they were receiving G.C.H. injections but who were actually receiving water injections.

Meal substitutes

Meal substitutes have been much ballyhooed in recent years. Judging by the sex appeal of those who plug these products, I bet thousands of women take meal substitutes in the hope that they, too, will become sexy.

Meal substitute packets contain, for the most part, dried milk powder, to which eight ounces of milk must be added. Almost three quarters of the nutritional value of meal substitutes comes from the milk that is added. Actually, you'd be just as well off drinking a glass of chocolate milk. A meal substitute contains approximately 13 grams of protein, 9 grams of fat, and 24 grams of sugar, for a total of 230 calories, while a glass of home-made chocolate milk contains 10 grams of protein, 10 grams of fat, and 27 grams of sugar, for a total of 235 calories.

Meal substitutes promote weight loss because they contain 250 to 750 fewer calories than the meals they replace. These products contain neither an appetite suppressant nor a fat-reducing agent. Their effectiveness lies solely in the fact that they reduce your calorie intake.

The makers of meal substitutes recommend one packet for breakfast, one for lunch, and a supper of about 500 calories for a total of 1,000 calories a day. However, to lose weight more quickly, they suggest four meal substitutes a day, with no other food permitted. This 1,000-calorie-a-day diet is too rich in calcium for adults and may lead to health problems such as kidney stones.

Meal substitutes are useful primarily for people who skip meals and haven't the time to prepare nutritious food for themselves.

Fasting

Fasting to lose weight is no longer recommended, a diet of water alone having proven ineffective — even dangerous.

If you were to lose 33 pounds in one month of fasting, 7 of these pounds would be water loss, 13 would be muscle loss, and 13 fat loss. As soon as you resumed eating, the 7 pounds of water would quickly be regained. What's more, for each pound of muscle regained upon resumption of a normal diet, one pound of fat would automatically be added. So, even if you were to lose 33 pounds by fasting, you'd gain them all back.

The loss of muscle due to fasting has more serious consequences. After three to six weeks of fasting, signs of weakness appear. The heart, which is a muscle, grows weaker and begins to shrink; after about two months, it becomes paper thin. Death soon follows, as in the case of the Irish prisoners who went on a protest fast several years ago.

For those who view fasting as a personal, spiritual experience, I recommend a good checkup before starting, and that the fast continue for no longer than two weeks.

Fad diets

Miracle diets — carbohydrate diets, egg diets, grapefruit diets, the list goes on and on — are deficient in that they lack one or more of the essential nutrients of a healthy diet. Therefore, you cannot follow such diets for more than two consecutive weeks without risking illness.

The weight loss with this type of diet is dramatic; so, too, is the weight gain after the diet is over. As with fasting, the water lost is gained back in a short period of time. And, when you regain the muscle that was lost, the fat you shed is automatically gained back as well. These diets serve no purpose, unless you wish to lose four to seven pounds quickly.

Self-prescribed diets

People who go on a diet without sufficient knowledge are asking for trouble. Most self-prescribed diets are poorly balanced and too strict. Problems which may result from such diets include anemia, weakness, muscle loss, cardiac fatigue, and hypoglycemia.

I recall a young woman who came to see me one day in desperation. No matter how hard she tried, she couldn't lose her 33 pounds of excess fat. In the morning, determined to solve her weight problem, she'd have only two cups of coffee and three cigarettes. At noon, she'd stick to her diet and eat just a green salad and a tomato, washed down with two cups of coffee. Around 4 o'clock, she'd start to crack. Feeling weak, she'd lose her willpower and dive into the fridge like a woman possessed. She'd eat everything in sight — pastries, ice cream, you name it. Her binge would go on almost all evening. Then, afterwards, she'd feel guilty. Totally discouraged, she asked me if I should perhaps refer her to a psychiatrist. What she didn't realize was that her problem was not psychological, but physical.

The main problem with self-prescribed diets is that people often skip meals or eat meals that are too skimpy. As a result, their blood sugar level plunges, causing hypoglycemia with its host of symptoms.

If you have a weight problem, consult a doctor or a dietitian for sound advice on the type of diet you should follow.

Balanced diets

So-called balanced diets, of 1,000 to 1,200 calories a day, have long been recommended as the only ones that are really effective.

According to the medical literature, however, less than 5 percent of those following such diets are able to lose 30 pounds or more. These diets have proven effective only for persons who are less than 30 pounds overweight.

Diets of 750 to 1,000 calories are poorly balanced and may lead to serious problems. Because these diets lack sufficient protein, 25 percent of the weight loss is muscle. When the dieter begins eating normally again, not only is this muscle gained back, but an equivalent amount of fat is automatically tacked on. Over the short term, 50 percent of the initial weight loss is thus regained. More important, the muscle loss poses a serious health hazard.

Special protein diets

Protein diets have been tested for over ten years in France, England, Germany, and the United States. These diets promote fat loss without any loss of muscle tissue. However, because they provide only 300 to 600 calories a day, such diets produce a change in the body and result in a condition known as ketosis.

The protein eaten in these diets can take several forms: meat, fish, or chicken; special protein supplements in powder or liquid form; or, a mixture of food and special proteins.

The advent of protein diets marked a turning point in the development of slimming techniques and in our understanding of physiology, the role of insulin, fatty acids, ketone bodies, and the storing of proteins.

Whereas conventional diets are successful in only 5 percent of cases in which patients have 40 pounds or more to lose, a 1976 report published by the Harvard University medical team of Dr. George Blackburn and Dr. Bruce R. Bistrian showed that protein diets are far more effective. In a study of 650 patients covering a period of four years, 75 percent of the subjects were able to lose 30 pounds or more on a protein diet, and 30 percent were able to maintain their weight loss after four years.

Figure 5

COMPARATIVE SUCCESS RATE FOR LOSS OF 40 POUNDS OR MORE (DR. BISTRIAN)

1,200 calorie diet	5%	After 4 years	2%
Protein sparing modified fast	75%	After 4 years	30%

In addition to following the prescribed diet, all the subjects in the study took a behavior modification course designed to help them maintain their weight once their excess pounds were lost. The results were so good that they prompted doctors to change their conventional methods of treating obesity.

In 1977, forty Americans reportedly died from a diet composed exclusively of predigested liquid protein (hydrolyzed collagen). These deaths provoked a public outcry concerning the dangers of such a diet. (In 1977 alone, four million people took this protein in the United States.) An exhaustive study of these deaths was conducted by the Center for Disease Control in Atlanta. The findings of Dr. Arthur Frank and Dr. C. Graham of the Faculty of Medecine of George Washington University, as published in the prestigious International Journal of Obesity, indicate that of the 40 people who died, 32 were receiving either inadequate medical supervision or no supervision at all. (Liquid protein was available in the U.S. without a prescription.) These patients were lacking in both minerals (potassium, calcium, magnesium) and protein. The four others had heart problems.

Protein diets are effective for three reasons:

1- They result in a rapid weight loss of 13 to 26 pounds a month and thus motivate the patient to continue the diet.

2- They produce a feeling of well-being due to the ketosis effect.

3- They result in a loss of appetite, again due to the natural effect of ketosis.

For people with a serious obesity problem who have never been able to lose weight, this type of diet, in conjunction with a behavior modification program, will give excellent results in three out of four cases.

A warning: One should not go on a protein diet unless supervised by a physician experienced in this kind of treatment. When administered by an expert, special protein diets are not dangerous and are certainly preferable to remaining obese.

Modern society has led us to believe that we can become happier by stuffing ourselves. At the same time, however, medical science has made us aware of the dangers of overeating and has given us the means to win the battle of the bulge. Will we ever develop a diet more effective than the ones we have now? I doubt it. The problem is no longer one of nutrition, but one of behavior, and it is on this latter subject that we must now focus.

CHAPTER 7

BROADENING YOUR HORIZONS

A few inches from success

The late Dr. Wilder Penfield was director of the Montreal Neurological Institute for several years and a scientist of international repute. One day, during a symposium at the National Academy of Sciences in New York, he shared the following discovery: certain regions of the brain store in memory all the past experiences of a person, even if he no longer remembers them.

While performing a brain operation on a fully conscious patient, Dr. Penfield stimulated an area of the brain with an electrode. Immediately, the patient began reliving a long-forgotten incident from his childhood. The experiment was repeated on several subjects, with the same results. The subjects actually relived entire experiences, even though they had been forgotten for years. Once again they could see in minute detail the people and surroundings of a time past. They could hear the words and sounds; they could feel the objects around them and smell the odors. They even experienced the same emotions they had felt at the time.

This discovery stunned psychologists and doctors alike. How could the brain store so much information? The English neurophysician W. Grey Walter theorized that the brain contained at least ten billion cells and that it functioned much like a computer.

His research as well as that of many others will lead the way to the greatest revolution ever known in the fields of psychology, psychiatry, and medecine. With the development of computers, man has finally begun to understand how the brain works.

Between our ears is a six-inch computer, the most powerful on earth. This computer, known as our subconscious, registers everything we experience and keeps an up-to-date record of all our successes and failures. It is this record of how we fare in life that determines our self-image. Everything we do, all our actions and behaviour, depends on this mental image we have of ourselves.

If you have a positive self-image regarding certain activities such as dancing, painting, or cooking, if you have confidence in your abilities in these areas, you'll be brimming with self-assurance when you engage in these activities and will succeed easily. Success breeds success.

On the other hand, when faced with a situation where you have not had any past success, either because it's a new situation or because you have failed in the past, the mental image you have of yourself will be negative, your confidence in succeeding, nil. Your attitude will be to avoid taking action if possible, because you consider yourself incapable of succeeding. Or, you may try to deal with the situation, but with a very negative attitude, in which case your lack of enthusiasm and determination will undoubtedly lead to failure. This failure will then reinforce your belief that you're not suited to the task. Failure breeds failure.

Right between your ears, however, is that powerful six-inch computer. All you need to do is program it properly. If you were to fill the Empire State Building with the most sophisticated computers available and connect them together to increase their power, you wouldn't be able to match the power of the one you have in your head. Your subconscious is 200,000 times more powerful than any man-made computer. It has been estimated that most people use only one to three percent of their brain's potential.

Man was created to be happy and successful. He has everything he needs to succeed: his body is an extraordinary machine no robot can match, his brain, a source of almost infinite power. And yet, with all his potential, man is perpetually unhappy. Why? Why does he insist on abusing his body? Why does he insist on getting sick? Why is he satisfied with less, when it is within his power to make all his dreams come true? Man was created to be happy and successful.

Bad programming

The negative influence of society and our own negative thoughts have been progamming us in a counterproductive way. Without our realizing it, we have been focusing our attention only on the negative. We can no longer see the bright side of things, only the dark. We feel no sense of accomplishment in doing our work well; we believe it's normal that we only do our jobs satisfactorily. On the other hand, we consider it catastrophic, unforgivable, and unthinkable to make even the smallest mistake.

When we do happen to slip up, our subconscious immediately records the error, which is amplified and intensified by the emotion we associate with it. Our self-image becomes tarnished. We think to ourselves: "I'm a loser, a good-for-nothing.'' And all because of a small mistake. That we may have also had nine great accomplishments doesn't seem to matter.

Lack of self-confidence

Last week, Suzie B. came to my office for the first time. Aged twenty-two, she was 79 pounds overweight. Suzie seemed a dynamic, interesting and cheerful woman. Despite her young age, she assumed heavy responsibilities at her job, running the accounting department and supervising four employees. At first sight, I was quite impressed. ''Here's a talented woman,'' I thought to myself. ''She should be able to solve her weight problem easily.''

Upon reading her questionnaire, I discovered that she had been on diets since the age of thirteen. She told me she had tried everything: home-made diets, European diets . . . she had even gone to London where, in a clinic with no doctor but with daily supervision, she had managed to lose 36 pounds in 20 weeks by following a 750-calorie-a-day diet. She quickly gained back all the weight, though, and had spent thousands of dollars for nothing. Each time it was the same story: she would lose weight, only to gain it back as quickly as she had lost it, despite normal eating habits.

Discouraged, she broke into tears. ''I'll never make it,'' she said. ''I don't understand how I can succeed in everything I do but be such a dismal failure when it comes to solving my weight problem.'' Firmly convinced that she could benefit from my program, I explained to her how I could help and told her there was a 90 percent chance she could solve her weight problem once and for all. I detected a hint of a smile and asked her if she thought it was going to work this time. ''I'm glad to see your enthusiasm,'' she replied,''and I have no doubts about your therapy. The thing is, I've always failed in the past. Well, okay, I'll give it one more try.''

How was it possible that an energetic young woman, who succeeded at everything she tried, could not succeed on a diet? Although she clearly possessed all the potential to succeed, her repeated failures had destroyed all her confidence in dealing with her weight problem. Whenever she began a diet, the odds were stacked against her from the start because she was convinced she would fail.

When I analyzed the reasons for her consistent failures since the age of thirteen, it quickly became apparent that all her past diets were deficient in protein. Because of this, the weight lost in muscle, probably about 25% in most of her diets, was gained back twofold after she stopped dieting, even though she returned to a healthy, balanced diet suited to her weight. We know that for each pound of muscle that must be gained back to maintain good health, one pound of fat is added automatically.

So, because of a physical problem — a poor choice of diet — Suzie had been programming herself negatively. She thought herself incapable of succeeding, while in reality the opposite was true, for she had all the necessary potential. She simply had to learn how to program herself positively to imporove her self-image and increase her self-confidence regarding her new diet.

Perfectionism

In one of my courses on behavior and motivation, I asked one of the participants, Sandra, to recount her accomplishments of the previous week.

"I haven't done anything good — I don't know what's wrong with me. I try hard but nothing works."

"You must have at least had one experience that gave you satisfaction."

"No, absolutely nothing. I hate myself."

As I asked more questions, I learned that Sandra was disappointed with her behavior during a recent bowling party. After the game, she felt that nasty remarks by a member of an opposing team had been directed towards her. "We lost, but at least *we* were honest when counting our points," sneered the disgruntled opponent. Sandra, very honest by nature but also highly competitive, felt her blood boil. On another occasion she might even have come to blows, but this time she controlled herself and merely smiled, rationalizing that defeat was more difficult to accept than victory. The evening ended without further incident. She returned home, quite pleased with herself, but then, as she had done so often in the past, she automatically headed for the refrigerator and began stuffing herself with chocolate cake.

Sandra was disgusted with herself: "What a fool I am! I acted well at the bowling party and now, to reward myself, I pig out on cake. I can't believe how stupid I am. You wanna eat, fatso? Go ahead! You make me sick." She ended up devouring half the cake. Sandra was furious with herself — she hated herself for cheating on her diet. This was her fourth diet, and each time it was the same old story. For several weeks she would adhere strictly to her diet; then, suddenly, she would start cheating. Next came the guilt feelings, and it wasn't long before she dropped her diet altogether and gained back the weight she had lost.

Despite her failure to lose weight, Sandra had the potential to succeed; it was simply a case of poor programming. When asked about the positive events in her life during the previous week, she couldn't think of any, when in fact there were several: she had stuck to her diet at least five out of seven days; she had controlled her temper admirably at the bowling party; and, above all, she had attended her diet course even though she'd cheated. On the negative side, there was very little: all she had done was indulge herself with cake as a reward for having kept a cool head at the bowling party — certainly no reason to feel guilty.

Because Sandra's subconscious recorded only negative things, to the exclusion of almost everything positive she accomplished, she had a very poor self-image: "I'm a loser — I can't even resist a small piece of cake." Sandra never gave herself credit for all her strong points, which far outnumbered her weak. She programmed herself negatively because she felt that a person was either a winner — perfect in every respect — or a loser. There was no in-between.

Sandra didn't allow herself to cheat because she felt that unless she was perfect, she wasn't worth a damn. She felt guilty for being so weak when it came to dieting. Her programming was all wrong. Like everyone else, she wasn't perfect and was capable of making mistakes. What she had to do was program herself in such a way as to include the right to cheat from time to time. She could then learn from her errors and improve herself.

Hope

Modern psychology is marvelous in that it provides us with insights into human behavior and enables us to improve our own behavior by using the appropriate techniques.

Freud and his followers are completely outmoded. All their theories were based on dredging up incidents from the patient's past. The patient would lie down on a couch and recall events from his life, with very little positive input which could foster recovery. Modern psychology offers an alternative to these methods by focusing more on the future and on the imagination. Man is learning to program himself in a positive way.

The old school of psychology dealt primarily with problems, whereas modern psychology puts greater emphasis on solutions. You can program and deprogram yourself at will. If you have a strong desire to change, to feel good about yourself, you can succeed. We'll provide you with all the necessary tools to reach your goal. If you're the kind of person who prefers solutions to problems, this book is for you.

Enthusiasm

Zig Zigler, a well-known American authority on motivation and communication, once related the following true story. A school principal was having difficulty finding a teacher who could work with a class of "problem students" — slow learners who were also hyperactive. Three teachers had already tried and failed, so the administration was now seeking a fourth. A young woman applied for the job and was hired. A few months later, the students had made astounding progress. Their grades were excellent, which was totally unexpected, and their discipline was also quite good. The school principal called the teacher into his office and asked her the reason for her extraordinary success. "It's only natural, sir. You gave me good students. They all have IQs between 115 and 130. So I'm enthusiastic and I push them a lot. That's why they're successful."

What happened was that she'd seen a class list with numbers on it which she'd assumed were the students' IQs. In fact, they were the students' locker numbers. Thinking the students highly intelligent, she treated them enthusiastically and motivated them as much as possible. She would repeatedly tell them: "I know you can do much better than that." Their results were but a reflection of the enthusiasm shown by their teacher.

Enthusiasm is the key to success. You must face your problem the same way the teacher faced her "problem students." You know you can do better. Each morning, upon awakening, look at yourself in the mirror and say with a smile: "Nothing, nobody, will spoil my enthusiasm today." Success is easy if you believe in it.

CHAPTER 8

DEPROGRAMMING

A past life

Joan was 26 years old. Highly intelligent, she held a university degree in psychology and was teaching full-time. Her free hours were spent reading, especially books dealing with the occult and psychology. She was 5 feet 4 inches tall and weighed 200 pounds, almost 80 pounds of which was excess fat.

For years, Joan had been attempting to lose weight. There wasn't a diet she hadn't tried. First she went on a diet where she ate only eggs, then, on a diet where only bread was allowed. This was followed by a milk diet, a pudding diet, and a milk shake diet. She even tried a banana diet. Joan always gave up after the first few weeks; her longest diet lasted a month.

It was almost by chance that she came to see me. One of Joan's friends persuaded her to go on a diet and helped her become more aware of her enormous potential.

When Joan began her new diet, I told her to imagine herself at her ideal weight, engaged in some kind of physical activity she enjoyed. She was unable to do so. Ironically, she carried with her a photograph taken five years ealier in which she was pretty and slim. Even with this picture, she couldn't see herself as she once was. I advised her to keep on trying, and to focus on the final result.

To succeed, you must have a clear picture in your mind of the goal you wish to attain. Unless your objective is well defined, it's almost impossible to reach it. You always find what you're looking for.

By her fifth visit, Joan had already lost twenty pounds. Everything was going well: she never felt hungry on her special protein diet, and she was in better shape than ever before. I congratulated her but she didn't seem too enthusiastic. Just before the end of our consultation, she stood up and, looking somewhat ill at ease, said: "I read an article this week that we all have past lives. If I'm fat now, it's because I starved to death in my previous life. I'm dropping my diet because I want to die fat and happy this time around." With those words, she disappeared out the door.

I was dumbfounded. How could a young woman with so much going for her behave this way? Why wasn't she using her potential to program herself for success? The problem was that she was unable to imagine herself thin and to visualize her goals clearly. All she wanted was to feel a bit better by losing a few pounds — then she could drop her diet.

Mental blocks

Something was preventing Joan's subconscious from being programmed positively. She obviously had a mental block. We may never know what caused her psychological block, and she probably doesn't know herself, but as long as she had it, her potential would remain locked up inside her. She had no chance of succeeding unless her psychological block was removed.

So far in this book, you have become aware of your almost limitless potential. However, in order to achieve concrete results, you must rid yourself of your psychological blocks which are preventing you from programming your subconscious properly. We'll be discussing this subject in the next twelve chapters. The last part of this book will be devoted to efficient programming techniques that will guarantee your success.

Do you have a mental block?

I wouldn't say that everybody has mental blocks, but at least 90 percent of those reading this book probably have one or more mental blocks that are preventing them from losing weight. The trouble is, most people are unaware of them. The only way to identify mental blocks is through careful analysis. This is what we'll be discussing in the following pages.

One way of finding out whether or not you have mental blocks is to examine how you behaved during previous diets. If you were usually successful for several weeks or months, and then, suddenly, for no good reason, you lost your motivation and started cheating, unable to control yourself no matter how hard you tried, there's a good chance you're suffering from a mental block that is preventing you from making further progress.

Another way of determining if you have a mental block is to try to imagine yourself at your ideal weight, wearing the kind of clothes you'd like to wear and doing some kind of activity you dream about. If you can't create this scene in your mind, as though it were actually taking place, a psychological block is probably standing in the way.

You must look for your mental blocks systematically. Often they have been hidden for many years. Some people have only one mental block, others several. So, even if you've identified one, keep looking in case there are others.

At times you'll hear people say: "I eat to compensate for other things." Indeed, people with a psychological problem often try to cover up their hurt with fat. When an attempt is made to lessen this hurt by dieting, it only hurts more, causing a mental block which prevents the obese person from shedding his excess weight. Once you're aware of a psychological wound, you must heal it naturally and not conceal it with a cushion of fat.

If your overeating is a form of compensation, you may need the help and advice of a doctor, counselor, or psychologist. Don't hesitate to consult one if necessary. It may spare you months or even years of doubt, frustration, and suffering.

Prescription

In order to ensure the best results in your search for your mental blocks, I suggest you read the next twelve chapters rather quickly, in one sitting. Then read each chapter again, slowly, taking notes as you go along. Ask yourself if you've been through experiences similar to those discussed in the book. Finally, if you're still having a hard time identifying your mental blocks, take a chapter which you feel might be of help and read it before going to bed. You should also ask your subconscious the following question: "Do I have a mental block?" Ask yourself this question every night for a least three weeks. Be patient. The answer will come to you when you least expect it, naturally, as though you've always known it.

There's a saying that when you've identified your problem, it's already half solved. In the case of a weight problem, the other half may require the assistance of your doctor, counselor, or psychologist. Your subconscious, too, can play a vital role in helping you lick your problem. At least once a day for three weeks, preferably upon retiring in the evening, say to yourself: "I do not want or need mental blocks anymore. I shall concentrate only on the benefits to be gained by reaching my goal."

CHAPTER 9

SEXUAL BLOCKS

Dormant sexuality

Darlene was a 54-year-old widow who had been coming to see me almost annually for 10 years. When she married at age 20, she was a bit on the plump side, but five pregnancies in the first five years (she had three boys and two girls) caused her to put on considerable weight. Despite several diets, Darlene now tipped the scales at about 300 pounds.

Each time Darlene went on a diet, it was the same story. She would lose considerable weight the first month, but a mental block would cause her to give up shortly thereafter. Then I wouldn't see her until a year later, at which time all the weight she had lost would be gained back, along with a few extra pounds. On two occasions she skipped her yearly visit to try other slimming programs, but the results were no better.

A charming and happy person by nature, Darlene was dominated for 30 years by an authoritarian husband. To her, this situation was normal: she had a good husband and owed him obedience. Shortly after the birth of their last child, her husband, who was very family-oriented, suggested that his sick brother move in with them. He was an epileptic and had no place to go. So, with exemplary devotion and plenty of good cheer, she raised her five children and cared for her brother-in-law.

The couple's sex life, however, was a big zero. Their bedroom was next to the T.V. room where, each evening, the brother-in-law would sit and watch the late-night movie till two o'clock in the morning. There was almost no privacy for sexual relations. The husband refused to ask his brother to change his habits, saying the poor guy was an epileptic and that watching T.V. was his only joy in life. Except for three or four times a year, then, the couple went quietly to bed without fireworks or fanfare. Darlene didn't seem to mind — she took the situation in stride.

Fifteen years later, Darlene's husband suffered his first heart attack. From then on, he could no longer maintain an erection. The couple came to my office a few weeks after the attack. The husband was no longer interested in sex and blamed his illness; Darlene said it was her fault, claiming that she was too fat to excite her husband. The result: no sexual activity for the next 10 years, until her husband died from his second heart attack. During her 31 years of marriage, Darlene did not appear unhappy. With time, she managed to sublimate her sex drive to the point where sex no longer interested her at all. Her sexuality was dead.

A few years later, Darlene was obliged to return to work. She met a man her own age who treated her kindly; and, much taken with his courtesy and attention, she quite innocently allowed him to woo her. After a few pleasant dates during which he remained the perfect gentleman, her suitor became more intimate. One evening, while at the movies, he put his arm around her and tried to kiss her on the mouth. Darlene recoiled in horror, burst into tears, and ran out of the theater. The poor man didn't understand what was happening and tried to console her, but to no avail. Finally, in desperation, he took her up to her apartment — the first time he'd ever been to her place. She was still paralyzed and continued sobbing.

After about ten minutes, her weeping subsided. Apologizing for her behavior, she confessed that she was fond of him and asked him to be understanding. She would explain later why she had acted so. With a shy peck on the cheek, she asked him politely to leave. Darlene spent that night sobbing into her pillow.

"Why did I react that way?" she asked me. I explained to her that her first kiss in thirteen years had awakened her dormant sexuality. She was unblocking.

Of course, everything didn't become rosy overnight. Darlene had to readapt to, what was for her, a new situation. First of all, she had to accept the fact that she was still entitled to a sex life. She had to stop feeling guilty about her sexuality and accept herself as she was, a sexual being whose likes and fantasies were perfectly normal. It was her previous situation that was abnormal. She had to realize, furthermore, that her sexuality was important to her full development as a woman.

Once she got beyond this stage, she had to develop confidence in her ability to make love. What may seem very simple to some people can cause others a great deal of tension and worry. For this reason, it is important that the partner be understanding, loving and patient.

Darlene's story had an extraordinary ending. She finally got serious about losing weight and, in five months, dropped 80 pounds. Morning, noon, and night, she imagined herself at her ideal weight. She saw herself in a beautiful dress, waltzing with her lover. Darlene was truly happy.

Compensation

Veronica, 51, weighed 187 pounds when she came to see me. Six months earlier, she had tipped the scales at 253. Although she'd managed to lose 66 pounds in four months, her progress had stalled. As she seemed unable to lose any more weight despite serious efforts, we began looking for a mental block. When I asked her if it might be a sexual block, she began fidgeting and seemed to want to avoid the subject.

Veronica had been married for 25 years and rather late in life had a daughter who was now 12. At the time of her wedding, she weighed 132 pounds. She and her husband were sexually compatible at the start: he was a former priest and had no strong sexual inclinations; she came from a family where sex education was very limited — in fact, the subject was rarely discussed — so she too had no great desire for sex and was quite content having relations about six times a year.

After her pregnancy, at the age of 40, Veronica suddenly felt the need for a more active sex life. Her husband's interest in sex remained minimal, though. Shortly thereafter, her husband, who at age 50 was 10 years older than Veronica, began having problems with his prostate gland. Veronica tried everything to arouse him: sexy clothes, soft music, massages. But he never reciprocated. Never did he caress or kiss his wife or whisper sweet words in her ear. He did manage an erection at times, but was unable to maintain it. He felt inadequate and refused to discuss his problem. Whenever the time came to make love, he was overcome by his fear of failure, of not being able to perform.

Since Veronica never reached orgasm, she would leave the bedroom in frustration and watch television in the den until early morning. While in front of the tube, she would eat anything she could lay her hands on: cakes, cookies, chips, ice cream. Thus began her obesity problem. Veronica had trouble admitting that eating was simply her way of compensating for her unfulfilled sexual needs. She looked for all kinds of excuses and claimed that her eating was nothing more than a habit.

Veronica loved her husband and would never dream of leaving him or of seeking a sexual outlet elsewhere. She needed plenty of help to understand her problem and to dissociate her sexual needs from food. She also had to be helped as soon as possible, for it wouldn't be long before she developed a serious health problem to go along with her sex difficulties.

Veronica had to learn to cope with a certain sexual loss. This loss could be offset, however, by engaging in other self-actualizing activities which could gain her the affection of those around her. I recall a similar case where a 50-year-old woman set for herself the goal of getting into the best possible physical shape. Later, she organized dance courses to help people her age become physically fit. The project snowballed, and she ended up with an unexpected commercial success. Another woman, aged 59, discovered by chance that she was an incredibly gifted painter. Two years later, she exhibited her works and attained the success that, until then, had always eluded her. What's more, she no longer needed to eat all the time and she lost all her excess weight.

Sex is important but not essential. If you have a sex problem, you shouldn't replace it with another problem, such as overeating. Self-esteem is what's most important in life: to be able to look at yourself in the mirror and feel good about yourself.

Endless suffering

Mona was a 33-year-old divorcee with an eight-year-old daughter. She was attending my motivation and behavior courses in an effort to lose 55 pounds gained two years previous.

The first two weeks were encouraging. A well-educated woman, Mona had taken psychology and personality courses, which seemed to help her. When she came to see me the third week, she told me happily that she had found her problem and proceeded to tell me her story.

At the age of 24, she married a man with whom she'd fallen in love. Much to her dismay, she learned during the honeymoon that her husband had no interest in sex whatsoever. Shortly thereafter, she discovered that he was a homosexual. Convinced that she could help him get rid of this "disease," she asked him to father her child. But things didn't work out as she planned: the arrival of the child did nothing to diminish his homosexual urges. So two years after the birth she obtained a divorce.

The first few months as a single parent were rough, but Mona was up to the task.

A year and a half later, Mona met another man with whom she quickly fell in love. She had a strong libido, and one and a half years of abstinence had been hard on her. After a few dates, the couple began living together, but the relationship lasted only a few months. Realizing that he was an unstable good-for-nothing who was interested only in living off women, she kicked him out.

The wound was reopened. Twice she had become involved with a man, twice she had been burned. Obliged to live alone with her daughter once more, she vowed never again to be taken in by a man.

A few years later, Mona met a man who seemed stable and conscientious. She fell for him immediately.

But it wasn't long before this relationship fizzled too, for it turned out he was an alcoholic. Once again she was deeply hurt.

Realizing that she fell in love too easily, and tired of being hurt all the time, Mona decided to put on weight. On a subconscious level, she said to herself: "If I'm fat, men won't be interested in me — I won't have to worry about falling for them and then suffering later on when things don't work out."

In the following months, Mona put on weight for the first time in her life — 55 pounds. Although her tactics worked — men were no longer after her — she then had a change of heart and decided she wanted to lose the weight she'd gained. That Mona seemed to understand her behavior was a plus: it would make the likelihood of success that much greater.

One week during her treatment she came to see me with a long face. She told me she'd invited a friend to her place and that he'd asked her to make love. Although she wanted to, she refused, thinking herself too fat and unattractive. The next day she felt deeply frustrated at not having accepted, so she compensated by eating. Then she felt guilty about her behaviour and, to punish herself, she ate even more.

Unfortunately, after the appointment was over, I never saw Mona again. Although she was able to view her problem objectively, she still needed considerable help. There was a lot of hope for her, but in order to succeed she had to use the right tools.

Mona could not hope to lick her weight problem without first tackling the underlying problem — her great need for affection, which caused her to fall for any man who showed interest in her. Mona was to blame for her own unhappiness. Instead of choosing the man she really deserved, she grabbed the first one who came along. Her relationships were thus doomed to failure, and each failure further eroded her self-confidence.

Mona underestimated her ability to maintain an interesting relationship with a man. Convinced that each new relationship would inevitably result in failure, she decided to give up men altogether to spare herself further suffering. She sublimated her sexuality and her need for affection, and put on weight to keep the men at bay.

Mona had to change her self-image regarding her sexuality and her relationships with men. Little by little, she had to regain her self-confidence by proving to herself that she could enjoy the company of a man without necessarily going to bed with him. Once she got to know a man better, she could decide whether she wanted a more serious relationship with him. She had to avoid falling in love at first sight, for in such cases it was not really the man that she loved, but love itself. Mona's need to be loved was completely normal; she simply had to be more prudent and realistic in matters of the heart. Love is something that must be worked on and cultivated.

The right question

Roberta was a married woman of 42 who weighed 220 pounds. She had three children, the youngest of whom was 15. At the beginning of her diet she quickly lost 33 pounds; then, suddenly, she developed a mental block. Over the course of several months, for no apparent reason, her weight went up and down like a yo-yo. She would lose a pound or two one week, only to gain it back the next. Despite her excess pounds, Roberta led an active life and was very involved in community activities. Finding her mental block wasn't easy.

Roberta was married to a sick man. Silent and withdrawn, he had depressions about once or twice a year. As he had been ill for many years, Roberta assumed the role of man of the house. It was she who made all the decisions and did all the physical work. At 5 feet 10 inches and 220 pounds, she was certainly capable of heavy chores.

One day she related an incident that had occured the week before: "I was driving down a narrow, unpaved road when my car got stuck in a hole. A man offered to help and took over behind the wheel, but he couldn't get the car out. A short time later, two other men offered assistance. While the first man remained behind the wheel, the other two pushed, but the car wouldn't budge. I was livid. I didn't want to push the car myself, because I didn't want the men to think of me as a bulldozer — I wanted to be regarded as a woman. The men couldn't free the car, though, so I had no choice but to help them push. I drove home with tears in my eyes."

Roberta had suddenly become aware of her femininity. In the past, her behaviour had always been more masculine than feminine. Now she realized that if she lost weight, she might have to separate from her husband, and this prospect frightened her. She held nothing against him — he was a sick man — but she needed affection just the same. She needed to be caressed, to feel like a woman. Separation was out of the question, though, as her religious upbringing wouldn't allow it.

In her mind, Roberta associated being thin with getting a divorce. She had a choice: either to remain fat and stay married, or lose weight and separate from her husband. Roberta had to view things differently. Her real choice was between remaining fat and sick — she was beginning to show symptoms of diabetes — and losing weight and becoming healthier. She needed to be objective about her obesity problem and to stop associating weight loss with divorce.

Roberta had to decide whether she wanted to be happier, married or not. To continue living with her husband was fine, as long as she stopped destroying and deforming herself to avoid separation. Did she want to live fully, in good health and at her ideal weight, with the satisfaction of having discovered her femininity? Sure, her marriage wasn't perfect, but whose is? Roberta had to stop confusing the issue. The choice she had was simple — if she but asked herself the right question.

Frigidity

In 1979, a 37-year-old mother of 4-year-old twins registered for one of my courses. Always cheerful, Diane was forever cracking jokes and relating humorous stories about her obesity.

One day she recounted an incident that occured while she was bicycling near her home. For no reason, a passerby had insulted her, telling her she needed a bicycle built for two. (Diane was 88 pounds overweight.) Much to his surprise, she turned around, drove up to the sidewalk, and punched him in the face, After uttering a few choice words, she got back on her bike and drove on. The man just lay there, stunned.

Diane hadn't taken kindly to the man's rude remark; and, she did want to lose her extra weight. After 10 weeks of dieting and courses, she managed to shed 11 pounds. That's as far as she could get, though. Every two weeks she'd lose a couple of pounds, only to gain them back the following week.

During my consultations with Diane, I discovered that her personality was quite different from the one I'd been accustomed to seeing in a group setting. Behind her cheerful exterior lurked a very negative character. For each positive thought, she had forty negative. She never looked at her strong points — she was too busy convincing herself that she was a good-for-nothing who couldn't even lose a couple of pounds two weeks straight, despite all the means we were placing at her disposal. I told her I believed in her and that she had extraordinary qualities and potential; it was simply a matter of removing the blocks that were preventing her from succeeding.

Diane had been slim until she became pregnant with her twins at age 33. Before then, she had been living a normal, happy life. Her pregnancy, which was planned, went smoothly; it was only during childbirth that she learned she had been carrying twins. She was stunned. Diane had trouble accepting the fact that she now had two children to care for. She had counted on returning to work as soon as possible, but the arrival of the babies upset her plans. A mother for the first time, and of twins yet, she felt like a prisoner in her own home.

The first months were difficult, but Diane was equal to the task. After a year, she decided to return to work, even if it meant only a part-time job for a few years. Her husband wouldn't hear of it. "A mother who loves her children belongs at home," he said. Diane was furious. "You'll pay for this one day," she thought.

Diane's behaviour changed completely overnight. No more going out; no more dancing, which she loved; no more bicycling; no more sex. She underwent a complete metamorphosis. Before then, she led an active life and truly enjoyed sex; now, she became lifeless, limiting her activities to taking care of her twins and engaging in sex as seldom as possible. In four years, she gained 88 pounds.

Diane discussed her mental blocks: "I always blamed my husband for the twins — he never told me there'd been twins in his family. It was all his fault. I'll never forgive him for making me stay home." To punish her husband, she had radically changed her behavior and had put on 88 pounds in four years. Her husband had always loved her liveliness, her looks, her sensuality. Now she would pay him back, with interest. She would be a good mother to her children, but a lifeless, fat, cold wife. And, as soon as the twins were a bit older, she would divorce him.

In the following weeks, I tried to discuss the matter of her husband and her twins in a cooler, less emotional manner. It wasn't easy. Diane had a tendency to exaggerate the negative side of things. When faced with a small problem, she would blow it all out of proportion and lose sight of the point.

Taking one problem at a time, I explained to her that it was not necessarily her husband's fault that she had given birth to twins. Even if she had known of the existence of twins in his family, she probably would still have married him and had children. As for her role as mother, she could not simply shirk the responsibility of raising her twins just because it wasn't convenient.

Good communication between husband and wife could have prevented their unhappy situation. After all, her husband had been very patient and understanding during her four-year sulk in order to ensure their children's happiness and, if possible, that of the whole family. He had even gone without sex for the sake of family unity. What's more, he was continually proving his love for her by the many small attentions he paid her, despite her cold behavior. It was no wonder she felt guilty about the situation.

Diane was a roller coaster of emotions. One week she was high, the next low. She didn't know which way to turn. Should she get a divorce, or shouldn't she? What scared her the most about separating from her husband was sex. "I'm afraid of myself — I'm afraid of all the foolish things I might do. It's been a long time." To give herself some time to think things over, she took a one-week vacation alone in Florida.

I didn't hear from Diane again for a few months. Then, one day, she showed up at my office. I was eager to hear how she was doing. Looking happy and relaxed, she told me she had enjoyed her trip and that everything was now clear to her. She really did love her husband and children. She had a long talk with her husband upon returning from her trip, and their relationship was better now than ever. She was no longer afraid of her sexuality and was able to express it as never before. "You know," she confided, "we have four years of catching up to do."

Diane took a part-time job shortly thereafter, but her return to work didn't prevent her from taking good care of her twins. She also decided to return to her pre-pregnancy weight, and did so in a matter of six months. Diane was finally exploiting her full potential.

Damned men

Amanda, 28, had lost over 100 pounds six times, only to gain back the weight on each occasion. Intelligent and pretty, she had an excellent job, but no friends. She seemed to enjoy being single and was an active feminist. Men were much too egotistical — her father and brother were ample proof.

Amanda was able to shed weight with remarkable ease. After 5 months on a 1,200-calorie-a-day diet, she lost 70 pounds. She also gave up some of the false notions she had about food. On previous diets, she always managed to lose weight, but not without great effort and frustration. She always felt different from others and couldn't reward herself with food as others did. While following my diet, however, she made great progress and no longer considered herself different. She realized that she was a normal person who needed to eat normally to be able to fulfill her potential and to give her maximum.

Amanda finally saw that it was her obesity that had made her feel different. She also realized that the price of eating cake was very high: no stamina, no energy, no sex appeal, no parties, no personal satisfaction. So Amanda decided to sacrifice the thing that was the least important.

Everything went well for the first five months of her diet. She never cheated, and each week the scales indicated further progress. Then, suddenly, Amanda skipped two appointments. When I phoned her to find out if everything was all right, she informed me that she had stopped her diet completely. "It's better that way," she said. I insisted that she come to see me at the office, and she finally agreed.

As soon as Amanda arrived for her appointment, she began spouting her hatred of men: "Damned men — they're all the same. They want only one thing — sex. Wham bam, thank you ma'am! What's the use of becoming slim — it'll only attract the wolves."

She had given up her diet after receiving two telephone calls in the same week from acquaintances at work who had asked her out on a date. No overt suggestion of sex had been made in either case.

Amanda had a very strict sexual upbringing. Her mother had always warned her about men — especially their insatiable appetite for sex. At 28, Amanda was still a virgin and extremely apprehensive about sex. Although she felt a need for sex — she had lots of sexual fantasies about men and enjoyed masturbating regularly — the idea of having intercourse with a man frightened her. Her fear of sex had caused her to adopt a hostile attitude towards men, and she put on weight to keep them away.

On the six occasions when she lost 110 pounds, she gave up her diet and gained back the weight because men began showing interest in her. Amanda was very pretty, so as soon as she became slim, men were attracted to her. Whenever a man called her up for a date, her sexual block would be triggered.

Jokingly, I predicted she would have her first sexual experience within a matter of months. She was not convinced: "It's impossible — in 28 years I've never had relations with a man, so why should I in the next few months?"

The ensuing months were charged with emotion. Once again, we had to dissociate the various aspects of her problem. Obesity was not the answer to her sexual problem — we had to deal with the question head-on. After discussing her mother's anti-sexual behavior in a compassionate manner, we looked at several sex manuals together and arranged for an appointment with a gynecologist, who gave her a clean bill of health.

When Amanda came to see me a few weeks later, she looked happy and relaxed. Proudly, she announced that she'd had her first sexual experience with a man, someone she'd known for several months. Of course, it had been a bit painful and she had bled slightly, but that was perfectly normal for a virgin. Her fear of sex had diminished; her confidence had grown. Another misconception had been discarded.

I then predicted that she would marry within a year and that she would bear at least two children. A look of astonishment crossed her face. "You and your predictions. I'll admit you were right last time, but now I think you've gone overboard. Why, just last week I wanted nothing to do with men."

Summary

Sexual problems are very common and come in many different forms. We've just examined six cases, no two of which were the same. Difficulties of a sexual nature are at the root of most weight problems. Obesity deforms the body, and the body plays a vital role in sexual expression. Some people will go to great lengths to avoid sexual relations: they may go to bed before or after their partner, complain that they have a headache, or say they're too tired — any excuse to avoid discovering the reality of their bodies. Whether they represent a sexual block or are the result of one, sex difficulties are at the heart of most obesity problems.

If you are overweight, you must ask yourself: "Am I fat because I have a sex problem, or do I have a sex problem because I'm fat?" You must ask yourself the right questions if you want the right answers. Read the case histories in this book one at a time and ask yourself: "Do I have this problem?" Ask your subconscious — it is a powerful tool which will provide you with the answer before you know it. Also, do not hesitate to consult a professional for help in gaining a clearer insight into yourself.

From experience, I can say that problems are rarely complicated — it is people who complicate them. There is a solution to every problem, but gaining weight is never the answer.

We have seen the case of Darlene, a 54-year-old widow who rediscovered her sexuality and lost her paralyzing pounds. Then there was Veronica, 51 years old, who learned to feel good about herself and to compensate for her sick husband's inability to satisfy her sexually by engaging in other gratifying activities.

On the other side of the coin, 33-year-old Mona, who went through one divorce and two separations, decided against learning to love, choosing instead to become obese in order to protect herself from further suffering. If she reads these lines, perhaps she will realize that loving is something that is learned, and that her choice was not really a choice at all as it will only bring her more suffering.

We also examined the case of Roberta, 42, who wanted to become the woman she really was by discarding the masculine behavior she had adopted because of her husband's depression. She must be careful, though, not to go to the other extreme. Perfect sex and perfect happiness do not exist, and separation is not necessarily the answer to all problems.

Finally, we discussed Amanda, who lost over 100 pounds on six occasions, only to gain back the weight each time. She was able to lose her unreasonable fear of sexual intercourse and gain more self-confidence.

Each of the above cases presented a different problem. There are surely many others. Whatever your problem, there *is* a solution, just as there was for each of the women we have discussed.

For every problem, there is a solution.

CHAPTER 10

OUT OF TOUCH WITH YOUR BODY

Happy-go-lucky

The doorbell rang. I awoke with a start and turned to look at the clock. It was 9:30 a.m. I had gone to bed very late the night before and was catching up on my sleep. As my wife and three children were away, I leapt out of bed, whipped on my bathrobe, and ran to the door. Standing there, with an irresistible smile on his face, was a vacuum cleaner salesman. An imposing fellow, he stood about 6 feet tall and must have weighed almost 400 pounds. Ordinarily, I would have slammed the door in his face, but this time I just couldn't bring myself to do it.

Speaking very politely, the salesman persuaded me to let him in for a demonstration. I invited him into the kitchen for a cup of coffee and asked him to make himself comfortable. He selected a chair, examined it carefully from several angles, and sat down. After a little banter, I told him I was a doctor who specialized in obesity problems. He burst into laughter. "That's a good one," he said, between two hearty roars. Intrigued by this portly gentleman, I tried to find out more about him.

"Pardon my indiscretion, but how much do you weigh?"

"No problem, doc. I don't know exactly — the last time I stepped on the scales was at my friend the butcher's. You see, it's the only place I can weigh myself. At the time, I weighed 466 pounds fully clothed — actually it was 466 and a half pounds," he grinned.

"You seem happy enough."

"Don't you think there's enough sadness in the world these days? I try to look at the positive side of things. I laugh, I eat, I live life to the hilt."

"Are you married?"

"I know it's rare nowadays, but I have a wonderful wife and I'm happily married."

"Does your wife have an obesity problem?"

"Not at all. My wife is much smaller than I — she's 5 feet 4 and weighs 220 pounds. I often warn her that she'll get sick if she doesn't eat enough," he laughed.

"Have you ever had any health problems because of your weight?"

"Nope. The best way to get sick is to go see a doctor. Nothing personal, doc, but I've never been inside a doctor's office. Do I look sick?"

"No, I must admit you seem to be in excellent health for an obese man of 55."

"Hey, doc, gimme a break, I'm only 28." Another hearty roar.

"For how long have you been a vacuum cleaner salesman?"

"Three years now. The competition's stiff, but we have the best product on the market. It's worth spending a bit more for quality."

"How did you end up in this line of work?"

"I had a hard time finding a job — people thought I was too fat. So, I decided to put my talents as a salesman to good use. I'm paid on a commission basis and I'm my own boss. I don't have to answer to anyone."

"How do people treat you?"

"Very well. I like people and people like me — as long as I don't break their chairs!"

"Are you doing well as a salesman?"

"I've been the top vacuum cleaner salesman in the area for the last two years. I'm not afraid of work. Climb a lot of stairs, too. I'm not sure you could keep up with me."

"You're very active, from what I see."

"Never stop. Last week I trained a skinny little guy for the company. He didn't last the week. Couldn't keep up with me. I rarely go to bed before midnight and I'm back on the road again at 7 o'clock the next morning."

"What's your secret for being the best vacuum cleaner salesman?"

"I'll tell you, doc. First of all, we have a good product, but that's not what really counts. You see, it's not the product that people buy — it's the salesman. When it comes down to it, I don't really sell vacuum cleaners — I sell myself. Incidentally, from the look of your carpets, I think you could use my services."

A few moments later, he'd sold me his top-of-the-line model.

"I've been a physician for 15 years and I've seen thousands of obese people. You seem to be the only one who is truly happy. How much did you say you weighed, again? Four hundred and sixty-six pounds?''

''Four hundred and sixty-six *and a half*,'' he chortled, ''fully clothed, at my favorite butcher's. Actually, doc, I have a confession to make about my weight. For about a month now, I've been thinking that maybe I'm too big. But had I come here this morning with a long face, I doubt you would've let me in. In order to sell myself, I have to sell my obesity. I might be unhappy about my weight, but I can't show it. Being a doctor, you know what it's like. If you have a headache or are a bit under the weather, you can't let your patients know. It's the same with a salesman — you can't let people know you have problems. You have to keep proving to yourself and to others that you're on top of the situation. You know, although I've always been fat, I never really though I was that fat until about a month ago. A customer invited me in and asked me to have a seat. I couldn't get into the chair, though, because of the armrests. 'If only they still made those big roomy chairs like in the old days,' I thought to myself. Then, while visiting another customer a few days later, I saw that she had one of those old-fashioned chairs and I was eager to try it out. As soon as I sat down, one of the legs gave way. Now I always examine a chair carefully before sitting down. You know, it's no fun carrying this carcass around day after day. I think it's about time I did something. I've had you as a client — now it's your turn to have me as a patient.''

One of the first revelations I had as an obesity specialist was that extremely obese people — those whose weight is two or three times above normal — have trouble seeing themselves as they really are. We often wonder how obese people let themselves become so fat. The truth is, they don't fully realize the extent of their weight problem. They avoid having their picture taken and refuse to weigh themselves; they often make their own clothes or have them made-to-mesure; and, when they look at themselves in the mirror, it's only from the shoulders up. Their vision becomes selective — they see only what they want to see. It's as if there were a split between the body and mind, with the body being viewed as simply a burden that must be carried around. Obese people try to hide their bodies behind a cheerful façade — they act jolly, smile constantly, and never say no. Instead of being themselves, they spend their lives going out of their way to please others. They're out of touch with their bodies.

Thin and depressive

It was the second day of my behavior course. I was explaining that if you want to get somewhere, you must first choose your destination — establish your goal — and then keep in mind the advantages of reaching this goal. Only then will you have the necessary motivation to persevere when the going gets tough. In the case of obesity, you must first decide on the weight you wish to attain, and then keep thinking of the benefits of reaching your desired weight.

Beth, a woman of 42, stood up. She was 5 feet 6 inches and weighed 280 pounds, twice her ideal weight.

"I don't see how losing weight would give me any advantage I don't already have," she said. "My obesity doesn't stop me from being happy."

"If that's the case," I replied, "why do you want to lose weight?"

"My legs, hurt, that's all."

I explained to her that if the only advantage she saw in losing weight was that it would provide relief for her legs, she would never reach her normal weight because she would stop her diet as soon as her legs felt better. Beth was offended.

"I don't understand you, Dr. Larocque," she said in an angry voice. "We pay for your course, we come to see you to get motivation, and here you are discouraging us. You tell me I'll never reach my ideal weight."

"If you don't think you'll gain anything by dieting, if you think dieting means only losing something — weight, habits, food, the pain in your legs — then unless you're a masochist, your efforts are doomed to failure. Nobody likes to lose — everybody wants to win."

"I've been fat since birth, and it's never prevented me from doing anything. Whatever thin people can do, I can do better. I belong to serveral social clubs, and it takes two skinnies to do what I can. I never refuse to do what's asked of me, but I can't say as much for others. I go bicycling. I enjoy swimming. I'm raising my three kids. I'm a member of the local P.T.A. committee, and, every weekend I go dancing with my husband."

"You're very active, but perhaps if you saw an advantage to losing weight, you could do as much, if not more, with less fatigue. And, what's more important, you'd be able to do all the things you enjoy for many years to come. You could stay young longer."

"I don't buy that. I believe you're born to be fat or thin, and that weight has nothing to do with illness. Anyway, thin people are always depressed."

"Do I look depressed?"

"You're different — you're the exception."

"I'm going to be honest with you, Beth. I'd like you to make a real effort this week to think of the advantages you'd gain by attaining your ideal weight. Write them down on a piece of paper and we'll talk about them later. If you can't come up with one good reason for losing weight, I suggest you drop everything now — you'd just be wasting your time."

Beth was seething. She returned home that evening in a rage and told the whole story to her husband, who, incidentally, was thin and tended toward depression. He listened to her for a long while without daring to say a word. After about half an hour, he looked her in the eyes and said, "Your doctor's right." She ran to the bedroom, slammed the door, and flung herself on the bed. Staring at the ceiling, she debated whether or not to continue with the weight reduction program. After a sleepless night, she decided to stick with the program and to think of how it could benefit her.

All of this happened eight months ago. Since then, Beth has lost 80 pounds. Her legs no longer hurt, but she's continuing with her diet just the same. Last week I asked her to find a photo of herself at her fattest and to write down on the back all the disadvantages of being so obese. She returned this week with with photo and the list of drawbacks:

1- tire more easily
2- lack of feminity
3- relations with others cold and difficult
4- unable to say no

I looked at her and said: "We've come a long way in eight months, haven't we?"

"Yes, but it wasn't easy. It's tough to accept the fact that you must change yourself completely. It's like moving a whole house — tearing it off its foundations and putting it somewhere else."

People who have always been very fat can easily lose touch with their bodies. From an early age, they learn to defend themselves by disregarding their bodies; they must continually prove that they have no handicap. Such individuals often engage in activities where they know they'll do very well, or specialize in a field where they can prove they're the best. They concentrate on intellectual pursuits and rarely, if ever, participate in sports or other physical activities.

Spiritual life

Louise was a 35-year-old mother of two children. She was deeply religious — her entire life was based on high moral values, which she tried to instill in her children. She never participated in sports, never did any physical exercise, never went swimming or dancing. She had nothing against these pursuits — it was just that in her scheme of things, physical activities were inconsequential. She was totally unaware of her body's need for exercise. Louise weighed 222 pounds, 100 pounds over her ideal weight. She was a perfect example of someone who was completely cut off from her body.

After reading one of my articles on motivation, in which I state that some people take better care of their cars than their bodies, Louise realized that she'd lost touch with her body. She discussed the origins of her mental block:

"At the age of 16 I was already fat. My mother had to make all my dresses. I can still remember her air of disgust when she ordered me to 'turn around.' I was convinced my body was ugly. Then I started to study continuously, to develop the intellectual and spiritual side of me. My body was no longer important."

I sincerely believe that a human being has three sides: the physical, the intellectual, and the spiritual. One does not go without the others. I do not feel you can truly enjoy a full spiritual life if you ignore the physical side of your being. Those who try to do so are only fooling themselves. We've all heard the saying: "a sound mind in a sound body." People who concentrate on the mind only, to the exclusion of the body, don't know what they're missing.

The body is a dynamo that supplies energy to the brain. The more the body works, the more energy it feeds to the brain, and the better the brain works. If the body is well taken care of, it will function longer — and so will the brain. Unfortunately, people tend to appreciate a healthy, vigorous body only when they no longer have one.

Louise got back in touch with her body. She lost all her extra weight and now goes bicycling and swimming with her husband and children. Her family life, which used to be good, is now even better. She enjoys using her body, and has found that the development of her physical side has added new depth to her spiritual life: "Ever since I discovered my body, I've started to discover my true spirituality."

Fashion

About a month ago, Billie came to see me for the fifth time in order to lose weight. Each time, she wanted to slim down for a special occasion: a trip, a wedding, or a party. She never remained at her desired weight, for as soon as the special occasion passed, she quickly gained back the weight she had lost. Billie was now 66 pounds overweight.

"My daughter is getting married in August, so I have to fit into this lousy dress I bought," she said angrily as she strode into my office. "I was comfortable at my weight, and now I have to slim down. Would you believe I couldn't find one lousy dress in my size? Damn fashion! Why do we always have to wear the latest style? It's not easy being a woman, you know. Society puts all this pressure on us. Of course, men don't have this problem."

"Do you feel you have to lose weight just to be in fashion?" I asked incredulously.

"Sure. When you go out, everyone looks at you. And if you're not well dressed, you're a laughingstock. It's not the same for men."

"It seems to me that losing weight should be a matter of personal choice, and that being in fashion should be another choice."

"I don't want to lose weight. I feel fine the way I am."

"But this is the fifth time you've come to see me to lose weight!"

"I know, but it's fashion that's forcing me to slim down. All the nice clothes are made for thin people. I can't let myself be out of fashion."

The first sign that you're gaining weight is not the scale, not shortness of breath, not fatique — it's your clothes. When your shirt or blouse starts pinching, it's time to do something. You're often more in touch with your clothes than with your body. However, I don't think you should decide to lose weight merely because your clothes have become too tight, or that you should stop slimming down — if you haven't yet reached your ideal weight — simply because your clothes fit better. I don't believe you should ever feel obliged to lose weight, whether it be for the sake of fashion, your spouse, or even your health. Losing weight should be a personal choice, made by yourself and for yourself.

The last I heard, Billie still wasn't in touch with her body and hadn't lost any weight.

For myself

Recently I was invited to a reception at which there were several hundred people present. At one point during the evening, I found myself dancing with a woman whom I'd never met before. She was obese — she looked to be about 5 feet 4 and must have weighed between 185 and 200 pounds. When I introduced myself, she stopped dancing for a moment, looked at me, smiled, and started dancing again. Her curiosity aroused, she began asking me questions about various diets, the meal substitutes advertised on T.V., the dangers of obesity, and the value of dieting. When the music stopped and I tried to get away to join my wife, she said, "I don't believe in your gimmicks. I like being fat and I'm going to stay that way."

When I told her I respected her choice and that my goal was to help only those people who wanted my help, she burst into tears. I handed her my handkerchief, accompanied her to her table, and excused myself.

A few days later a woman named Lana came to see me for a consultation. It was the woman I'd danced with at the party. I told her I was surprised to see her, considering what she'd told me about preferring to remain fat.

"I don't know what to think anymore," she said. "I thought maybe you could help me understand myself. I've been married for 20 years and have three children. When I got married, I was only a little plump — it was my pregnancies that caused me to gain weight. I feel fine this way, but my husband has been nagging me for several years to take off some pounds — he even threatened to get a mistress if I didn't shape up. I don't think my husband loves me!"

"On the contrary, I think he loves you," I replied.

"If he really loved me, he wouldn't love me just for my body."

"Your husband has been faithful up to now. He's a good father and a hard worker. From what you've told me, he seems to be a pretty understanding guy."

"Yes, that's true."

"If he didn't love you, he would have left you a long time ago."

"He often tells me he loves me, but I don't believe him. I want him to love me for myself, not for my body."

"For me, the body is as important as the mind. Nobody has the right to neglect it or mistreat it."

"If he suddenly went bald, I wouldn't threaten to find another lover."

"And he probably wouldn't either if you went bald. When faced with a condition that can't be helped, you react differently. However, if you neglect your body and don't respect it, how do you expect your husband to respect you? If you let your body go, you're letting your whole self go."

"But I'm happy the way I am."

"I think your husband loves you very much. His threats are simply his way of waking you up, of motivating you to live a fuller, more satisfying life for both your sake and that of your family. A human being is truly happy only when he gives everything he has, when he lives life to the hilt. Why be satisfied with less when you can have more?"

Lana began her diet at the time I was writing this book. I don't know what the future holds for her, but I sincerely believe you must be completely out of touch with your body to expect to be loved only for your mind. Together, the body and mind form a unique whole; one cannot be separated from the other without destroying something beautiful.

If we are God's creation, our first duty is to love ourselves — both body and mind. Then we'll be able to love others and be loved in return.

Summary

Obese people who have never been thin and who often weigh more than twice their ideal weight must beware of losing touch with their bodies.

Our vacuum cleaner salesman spent his whole life selling himself in order to prove that he could be obese without being a loser. He was never true to himself, though, and spent his life laughing when he didn't feel like it, being cheerful when he felt like crying, and saying yes when he really felt like saying no.

Beth was a regular whirlwind of activity, forever trying to prove to herself that her obesity wasn't a handicap.

Louise began to truly understand her spirituality only when she got in touch with her body. Her family life improved as well.

Billie didn't get back in touch with her body. She didn't want to admit that she had a problem; instead, she blamed fashion.

I think you must have your head in the sand to believe you should be loved for your mind alone and not for your body. As if you could exist without your body!

I know an entire family whose members have lost touch with their bodies. The mother is 62 and weighs over 220 pounds. Her motto is: "As long as the skin stretches, what's the use of losing weight?" She is literally paralyzed, spending almost all her waking hours in a chair, doing nothing. She would get out of breath tying her shoelaces—if she could reach them. Her husband, 61, weighs 264 pounds and is equally adamant about losing weight. "As long as the skin stretches . . ." He has a bad heart and pops about 12 nitros a day. Their only daughter still lives with them, a 33-year-old who tips the scales at 220 pounds. She has a high blood triglyceride (fat) level and is an excellent candidate for circulatory problems and diabetes. But, as her mother says, "As long as the skin stretches, what's the use of losing weight?" As if you could actually live without your body!

Do you take better care of your furniture, your clothes, and your car than you do of your own body?

CHAPTER 11

FEAR OF BEING THIN

Depression

Lilly was 48 years old and had been on a diet for two months. She was losing weight and was in high spirits when, suddenly, things turned sour. She looked tired, ate poorly all week, and put on weight. Why the abrupt change? While going through some old papers, Lilly had come across a photograph of her husband and 10-year-old son taken a short while before they were killed in a car accident 18 years earlier. She put the photo in a small frame and placed it on her night table. The photo brought back memories; she couldn't sleep at all that week, and her diet went awry. Seeing how much the photo was disturbing her, I asked her to remove it from her night table and to hide it somewhere.

The following week, Lilly was in good spirits again. She had taken my advice and was sleeping well. Her diet, though, was a disaster. "I don't know what's wrong with me,'' she said. ''It's as if a part of me refuses to diet. I have to struggle continuously.''

Although the emotions associated with the picture had dissipated, she couldn't stick to her diet. She showed me another photo.

''You asked me to find a picture of myself when I was slim. I found this one, but I never want to look like *that* again.''

Indeed, she did appear too thin in the photo.

''How much did you weigh then?'' I asked.

''About 80 pounds. This picture was taken one year after my husband and son were killed. I was in a severe depression for 18 months — that's how I became so thin. I had nightmares all last week — I kept seeing myself at 80 pounds, depressed, crying all the time.''

The cat was out of the bag. Lilly's mental block was her fear of depression and of returning to 80 pounds. In her mind, she associated losing weight with depression.

The simple realization that she was unconsciously associating weight loss with illness helped her considerably. She kept a diary in which she noted her thoughts and feelings about her life and aspirations. After a few weeks, it became clear to her that losing weight was not synonymous with depression; it was the accident that had caused her depression that, in turn, had caused her to lose too much weight. She also realized that losing weight did not necessarily mean becoming too thin. She felt reassured knowing that she could stop slimming down when she reached her ideal weight, and then remain at that weight.

Even when you finally see the light, it can still take several weeks to deprogram yourself. Normally, if you use the appropriate techniques, such as those described in chapter 8, the process takes from 4 to 21 days. You musn't assume that one day of positive thinking will be enough to wipe out years of negative thought patterns. It is necessary to write down your positive thoughts, repeat them time and again, and employ the suggested techniques to deprogram your subconscious. Even if your old ideas were totally harebrained, you must remember that your subconscious makes no distinction between good ideas and bad, so it must be deprogrammed.

The strong woman

Rachel, 49, was 5 feet 9 inches tall and had a solid build. She was 44 pounds overweight. Despite her size, she dressed elegantly and was very feminine. I had her undergo personality tests at the beginning of her slimming program and found that she was very aggressive and lacked self-confidence. As she didn't want to lose weight quickly, she chose a well-balanced, 1,200-calorie diet.

After three months, the results weren't too encouraging: she lost only 10 pounds. As she was rather down on herself, I suggested a stricter, 500-calorie diet, supplemented with proteins, vitamins, and minerals.

Rachel was reluctant and asked a lot of questions about the dangers of losing weight too quickly. She was afraid she'd become weak or sick. Although I reassured her and answered all her questions, she left my office with a worried look. She did want to lose weight, however, so she began the new diet despite her misgivings.

This time the results were good. In three weeks she lost 11 pounds, as much as she'd lost in three months on her previous diet. She felt great: she wasn't hungry and was so full of energy that she was even more active than she'd been before her diet.

When Rachel arrived for her next appointment, she began telling me how she had to become less belligerent. "I've got to cool it a bit," she said. She hadn't lost any weight that week; in fact, she'd gained a couple of pounds.

"How'd your diet go?" I asked.

"I cheated all week. I don't know what came over me. I wasn't hungry, but I felt I was missing something — I absolutely had to eat. In any case, I've never been able to get my weight any lower than it is now. I think I'd better quit."

Rachel's behavior was puzzling. At the beginning, she was really keen on losing her 44 pounds, but now that she'd lost half the weight, she wanted to quit. What's more, she said she had to be less belligerent. I asked her to explain.

"I have this aggressive streak, you see, and I have an explosive temper. I'll tell you something that happened last week. I was with my sister in a parking lot and I was trying to back up my car to get out of a spot. I couldn't though, because I was blocked by another car. Since the driver was in the car, I asked him politely to move it so I could get out. 'Whaddya, blind or something?' he said. 'There's plenty of room to back up!' I jumped out of my car and so did he. 'I'll show you who's blind! ' I shouted, and I punched the guy in the face. He hit the ground with a thud. A policeman came by and asked him if he wanted to file a complaint against me. 'Forget it,' he said. 'It's bad enough being beaten up by a woman.' "

Rachel certainly had an aggressive streak. She was quite proud of it too — I could tell from the way she recounted her story.

"Why did you tell me you had to cool it a bit?" I asked.

"If I keep losing weight, I won't be as strong. Then, if I don't watch my step, I'll end up getting my teeth knocked out."

Rachel then explained how she had become so pugnacious.

"The last time I was beaten up, I was 18 years old. I swore it wouldn't happen again. So I started pumping iron and I put on some weight. I became really strong — I could lift 135 pounds. There's no woman that can scare me, and very few men."

To feel worthy, Rachel had adopted the attitude that she had to be the strongest. For 30 years, since the age of 18, her strength was all that had mattered. "I'm the strongest," she'd say to herself. "I'm not afraid of anyone. Better not mess with me!"

When something, such as diet, threatened to diminish Rachel's strength, she panicked. She couldn't afford to lose the only thing she ever wanted in her life, the only thing that counted for her — being the strongest. Take away her strength and what did she have left?

A couple of events during the previous week had shaken her. For the first time in her life, she had to ask her husband to help her move a piece of furniture. "You're getting old," he teased. "You're not as strong as you used to be." Rachel felt deeply humiliated by these remarks. She didn't want to ask for help and tried everything to move the desk herself. She wanted to prove that she could still do it, but she couldn't. Then, when she had to ask her son to open a jar of pickles for her, it was the last straw. It was obvious that her diet was making her weaker, so she had to stop it. Her strength was what mattered the most — it was more important than her appearance, even her health. If she lost her strength, her ego would be destroyed.

Rachel's mental block had to be attacked from two angles. First of all, she had to realize that her diet was not making her weaker. Losing weight does not necessarily mean losing strength. It's not fat that gives us strength, but muscle, and Rachel wasn't losing any muscle on her protein diet, only fat. (A protein diet is the only one that promotes fat loss with no concomitant loss of muscle.)

Rachel also had to accept that she was getting older, and that this was the reason for her diminishing strength. She was approaching 50 and could hardly expect to be as strong as a 20-year-old.

That her strength would inevitably decline as she grew older was a bitter pill for Rachel to swallow, for it meant having to forsake the values she'd cherished all her life. It was now necessary for her to develop other qualities, to seek new outlets, and to program herself in a more realistic way, otherwise she'd be in for some pretty sad days.

A year later, Rachel took the same personality tests she'd taken at the beginning of her slimming program. The results of the first tests had revealed a very aggressive individual who lacked confidence and who tried to compensate for this deficiency by a show of strength. The most recent results, however, indicated a well-balanced character with plenty of self-assurance. Having become aware of her problem and, more importantly, having accepted it, Rachel established a new set of values and sought new goals. It wasn't easy — it took a year — but she made it. An energetic woman with a fine sense of organization and good social skills, Rachel joined the work force for the first time in her life and, at age 50, became a real estate agent.

Two years later, she was named her company's top salesperson. She had channeled her aggressivity in a positive way and had built up her self-confidence by setting a meaningful goal for herself and then working toward that goal. She's been at her ideal weight for two years now and has never been so happy.

Cancer

Maggie was 51 years old and weighed 160 pounds, 30 pounds above her ideal weight. Although slight of build, she had ballooned to 200 pounds before starting her diet —

her fourth. On her three previous diets she never managed to get below 160 pounds. She would carefully measure and weigh all her portions and would lose weight quickly — until she reached the 160-pound barrier. After persevering for a couple of weeks at that weight without making further progress, she'd get discouraged and begin cheating.

Maggie would get very upset with herself for not sticking to her diet. How could she be so good for three months and then give up so easily at the first minor set-back? She'd feel guilty for not having more willpower and, to punish herself, would eat even more. All her previous diets ended the same way. This one was no exception. However, this time she kept her next appointment despite having cheated.

What struck me immediately about Maggie was her strong guilt feelings. I explained to her that nobody else found her guilty of anything — she alone harbored these feelings. Her guilt was a very negative emotion which inevitably led to disappointment, more cheating, and giving up altogether. She had no reason to feel guilty because she wasn't guilty of anything other than being human. She couldn't expect to be perfect, for nobody is.

Being human, it was inevitable that Maggie would stray from her diet sooner or later, despite her good intentions. Like everyone else, she had habits and emotions that could not always be controlled by willpower alone. She wasn't Superwoman. I suggested that instead of feeling guilty, she try to learn from her mistakes to improve herself.

Whenever we slip up, we have an excellent opportunity to learn more about ourselves. Our habits are deeply ingrained reflexes whose existence we're not always aware of. People think they understand themselves well, that they know all their bad habits, when in reality they know little about themselves.

To lose weight, certain bad habits must be changed; but if we're unaware of these habits, how can we change them? We can't. And that's why most people who go on a diet eventually gain back whatever weight they lose: they don't change their bad habits.

Cheating on a diet, if we analyze the reasons behind it, can help us improve ourselves.

I asked Maggie to write down and repeat to herself every day: "I'm allowed to cheat, but not to give up." The following week she came to my office beaming with pride.

"It really works, Dr. Larocque," she said. "I had my doubts at the start — it was the first time anyone ever told me I had the right to cheat. Frankly, I thought you were nuts, but I followed your advice anyways and did what you told me to do. All week long I asked myself why I could never get below 160 pounds. Then, last night, it hit me — it was as if I'd always known the answer. Whenever I start looking thinner, I automatically begin thinking about my mother. I even dream about her. When I'm not on a diet, I rarely think of her, but as soon as I lose about 40 pounds and really start looking slimmer, I can't get my mother out of my mind. She was fat, you see, but then she lost too much weight too fast and ended up dying of breast cancer. It happened 20 years ago."

"Was your mother on a diet when she got cancer?" I asked.

"No, she never went on a diet. She just started losing weight for no reason, but she didn't go to see a doctor. It was only near the end that she sought help, but by then it was too late."

"It was her cancer that caused her to lose weight," I explained. "Paradoxically, you think that if you lose weight, you'll get breast cancer like your mother. In fact, you have a greater chance of getting the disease if you remain fat. It's now been established that there's a higher incidence of breast cancer among obese women."

Instead of blaming herself and punishing herself by eating, Maggie looked upon her cheating as an opportunity to learn more about herself. She sought the reasons for her mental block and found them.

Guilt is a negative, useless emotion that prevents us from succeeding; it can even cause us to regress. Maggie was not responsible for her mother's breast cancer, nor was she to blame for unconsciously associating weight loss with cancer. The only thing she was guilty of was being human, and to be human is to be fallible.

For 21 days, Maggie employed the deprogramming techniques outlined in this book and succeeded in overcoming her mental block.

Old age

Marina was a very attractive woman married to a health professional. She was 40 pounds overweight. Although she led a highly active social life, she never went out with her husband, for he worked five evenings a week and one weekend out of two. A member of various local organizations, Marina did lots of volunteer work. She had no children: her husband didn't want any because he didn't have the time to look after them, and she went along with him to please him. She was also afraid that a pregnancy would deform her body.

Marina's excess pounds were already beginning to mar her appearance, and this was one reason why she'd decided to lose weight. She also had another reason: she'd known for at least a year that her hard-working husband had a mistress. Through lack of communication during 12 years of marriage, Marina and her husband had destroyed the love that had brought them together. She no longer loved him, but she never let on that she knew about his extramarital affair. She was torn between the security of her 12-year marriage and the possibility of living a happier life with someone else.

For four months, Marina lost no weight at all on her diet, so we began looking for mental blocks. Each day, she'd ask her subconscious for the answer; one day it came to her. It was so obvious that we should have thought of it earlier.

"Each time I think about going on a diet, I break into a cold sweat. I get the uneasy feeling that if I lose weight, I'll get all kinds of diseases. What it comes down to is I'm afraid of looking older. I have several friends who lost weight and they look older now — their features are harder and full of wrinkles. Yes, I'm sure that's what's stopping me from losing weight. My skin's still nice, and I don't want to get wrinkles.

This fear of looking old, which prevented Marina from losing weight even though she disliked being obese and avoided pregnancy for that very reason, also prevented her from living a normal and happy life. When she envisaged the possibility of separating from her husband, she saw herself having to lose weight to attract another man. But if she lost weight, she'd look older and wrinkled — or so she thought — and she'd never be able to meet Prince Charming. So for fear of living alone under uncertain conditions, she clung to the security of her present situation.

The fear of wrinkles and of looking old is a very common mental block and is often found together with others. It's amazing how much more importance people attach to their appearance than to their health. Marina's health was poor, to put it mildly. Her blood sugar level was high — almost 200 mg % (up to 110 mg % is normal) — as was her blood triglyceride (fat) level. Her blood pressure was about 180/100 (120/80 is normal), and her heart was in pitiful shape. She was in great shape for a 75-year-old, but she was only 38.

You'd think awareness of her poor health would have prodded Marina into taking her diet seriously, but for the first month she was still more concerned about wrinkles. People usually don't appreciate things until they no longer have them, and Marina was not yet suffering from her health. Fortunately, by using deprogramming techniques and viewing things in a more realistic way, she finally succeeded on her diet. Previously, she had gone four months without losing a pound; now she dropped 44 pounds in three months.

To explain wrinkles, I usually use a balloon as an illustration. When inflated, a balloon is perfectly smooth, with no features or wrinkles. When deflated, however, it returns to its normal form and takes on its normal appearance. As you grow older, it's normal for your face to develop wrinkles. I've never known anyone, though, who didn't look younger after losing weight. Of course, if you spend hours in front of the mirror every day looking for lines, you'll get the impression after a week that your face is nothing but lines. You'll feel that your lines are becoming bigger day by day, and that you're getting more and more of them. Focus on a pimple on your face and the same thing will happen: it will appear three or four times bigger after a week of scrutiny.

People who lose weight have more spring in their step, dress more fashionably, and feel years younger. Don't let your youth slip away before you start appreciating it — it can take years to get it back.

Summary

Very often, losing weight is unconsciously associated with negative elements which prevent us from succeeding.

Lilly associated becoming thinner with excessive weight loss and depression. Rachel felt threatened by her weight loss because she thought she'd lose her strength which meant so much to her. When she finally changed her values, she became highly successful. Maggie unconsciously linked losing weight with breast cancer. When she learned to admit that she wasn't perfect, she was better able to understand her behavior, find her mental block, and deprogram herself successfully. Marina, tormented by an unsatisfactory marriage, was finally able to see more clearly into herself and to get serious about losing her unhealthy fat.

It is obesity that causes illness and premature aging, not losing weight. Don't give up — it takes years to regain your youth.

CHAPTER 12

CONDITIONING

Gluttony

When I ask people why they're overweight, one of the most frequent answers I get is: "I'm a glutton. I love to eat." That's the reply I got from Phoebe. Unable to stick to her diet, she'd tell me how much she enjoyed eating and that I didn't know what I was missing.

In an effort to find the mental blocks that were preventing her from losing weight, I asked her how things were going between her and her husband.

"I have a good husband," she answered quickly. "Everything's fine." I detected some uneasiness in her voice, as if she wanted to avoid the issue. Sensing that I may have struck a nerve, I insisted she tell me more.

"I have the best husband in the world," she snapped. "I couldn't ask for more."

"You're lucky to be married to the best husband in the world," I replied. "Surely he has a few small faults?"

"He's a good provider, he's faithful, he doesn't drink. I can't complain — after all, he's a man."

"And what's wrong with men?"

"Men are men. I've been married to one for 20 years, so I know what they're like. I'll tell you, one in my lifetime is plenty."

"Do you have sexual problems?"

"No, not at all. I just have to be available whenever he gets the urge. Since I'm pretty hot anyways, I don't complain."

"Do you have difficulty communicating with your husband?"

"Communicating? There's no communication at all. My husband's a strict, authoritarian man. He never says anything nice to me. In 20 years of marriage, not once has he ever told me he loves me. I feel like a piece of furniture in the house — sometimes I think he doesn't know I exist."

"Don't you consult each other on important matters?"

"I tried to speak up when we first got married, but it didn't work, so now I keep my moth shut and do what he asks. He's not blind — he must know the situation."

"Do you think food helps you compensate in some way?"

"Every morning when I get up, I have to prepare his clothes and make his breakfast and lunch. No smile, no thank-you. He just gets up from the table, grabs his lunch box, grunts, and rushes out the door. As soon as he's gone, I suddenly get this terrible urge to eat. So I head for the fridge and pig out. I can't help myself — I don't know what's wrong with me."

"Perhaps you're frustrated by your husband's attitude?"

"It hasn't changed in 20 years. I must be used to it by now. No, I think I'm simply a glutton."

In my opinion, there's no such thing as gluttony. It's normal to enjoy eating, but eating too much is another story. There are always reasons why we stuff ourselves and eat the wrong foods, but we are often unaware of these reasons. Certains habits become so ingrained that we're no longer conscious of them. "It's normal to eat a lot," we say to ourselves. "That's the way I am. I'm a glutton." We know we overeat, but we don't know why.

What made Phoebe eat excessively? Although she wasn't yet aware of it, it was her emotions. For 20 years, she'd been suffering from chronic frustration. She felt more like a servant and a maid than a beloved wife. She was suffering because she was afraid to stand up to her husband. Although he did appear authoritarian on the one occasion I met him, he loved his wife and couldn't understand why she was dissatisfied. He felt he treated her properly — that's the way things were done in his own family, and his mother never complained.

Phoebe had conditioned herself over 20 years to compensate for her chronic frustration by eating. All she knew was that as soon as her husband left for work in the morning — without even kissing her or thanking her for all that she did for him — she headed straight for the fridge. Not having made the connection between her frustration and her craving for food, she thought she was nothing more than a glutton. Her block was so strong that she couldn't stick to a diet no matter how badly she wanted to.

To solve her problem, Phoebe had two choices: she could continue being frustrated by her husband's attitude, but stop eating to compensate; or, she could simply stop being frustrated. As it would have been most difficult for Phoebe to remain frustrated for a lengthy period without eating, she chose the second solution, which was to get rid of her frustration.

Controlling an emotion such as frustration is not as easy as it sounds, for it involves changing one's way of thinking. Often, two people will react differently in a given situation because the thoughts they have about the situation are different. If you think differently, you feel differently. It follows, therefore, that if you wish to change the way you feel about something, you must change your way of thinking about it.

Phoebe thought that she couldn't speak up, that her husband didn't care for her, and that he considered her as nothing more than an object. As a result, she felt deeply frustrated. Phoebe had to change her way of thinking about her marriage. She had a husband who loved her but who, because of his upbringing, was unable to express himself. This did not mean, however, that she could not speak up and assert herself; she had the right to be herself, just as her husband had the right to be the way he was. Of course, it would be preferable if he acted differently toward her, but she had to accept him for what he was. Although he had a few faults, he also had many good qualities. By changing her way of thinking, by concentrating more on her husband's good points, by accepting the fact that he wasn't perfect, by thinking that it would be preferable if he were different, but that he had the right not to be, Phoebe managed to control her chronic frustration in a matter of weeks.

By being less demanding and accepting her husband the way he was, Phoebe became less emotional and less frustrated. She also stopped her compulsive eating. For the first time in her married life, she felt truly happy. She started communicating with her husband and explained her frustration to him without blaming him. He was stupefied — he had no idea she was suffering so much. Once he became aware of the situation, he made great efforts to improve his behavior.

Needless to say, Phoebe is no longer a "glutton" — she no longer feels compelled to eat because of frustration.

There are always reasons why we eat too much.

Just a habit

Glenda, 26, was married to her childhood sweetheart and had a 2-year-old son. At 220 pounds, she was considerably overweight. She suffered a great deal because of her obesity and had tried several times to slim down, but without success.

We tried for a month to find her mental blocks, but were unsuccessful. Glenda was an intelligent and stable young woman who had a normal emotional and sexual life. None of her personality tests revealed anything negative. She seemed perfectly normal, but fat.

I was stumped. How was it that someone with a strong desire to lose weight — and with no mental blocks to hinder her — couldn't succeed? Here's Glenda's story, as she told it to me:

"At home, everybody's fat. Obesity seems to be passed on from father to son or, in my case, from mother to daughter. It runs in the family. I weighed 11 pounds at birth, and I've always been fat."

"How do you spend your days?"

"My two-year-old keeps me pretty busy — he's always on the move. He, too, is already fat for his age. Like I said, it runs in the family. I never go out in the daytime, whether it's sunny or not. I'm more comfortable at home. Often I feel a bit blue in the afternoon, so I eat. It gets me through the day, and I enjoy it. At night, when it gets dark, I go out for a walk by myself. My husband looks after David."

Glenda was caught in a vicious circle. She'd been conditioned since birth to believe that her obesity was normal. As her parents used to say: "We're a fat family — we were born to be fat." Her brothers, her sisters, and both her parents were fat. It was in her genes — what could she do? I once had the opportunity to see her family eat; if I gorged myself like they did, I'd be fat too. But Glenda felt the way she ate was perfectly normal, and she fed her son the same way she fed herself.

Glenda was caught in another vicious circle as well. Ashamed of her obesity, she'd hide in the house all day and wouldn't even take her son out for a stroll, for fear of being ridiculed. With no outlet for her energy, she'd get the blues and would eat as a way of compensating. Eating was her only joy in life, apart from her son.

It is interesting to note how easily we become conditioned in our thoughts and behavior. If we accept an idea as true after being told repeatedly that it is (in Glenda's case, she was told by her parents that it was normal for her family to be fat), the idea becomes embedded in our subconscious as if it were carved in stone, and we never question it again — we just assume that it's true and continue to act on that assumption. Identifying your thought patterns and trying to change them can therefore be very difficult, but with the help of this book, you *can* do it.

The habit of eating to compensate for boredom is unconscious and involuntary. To get a clear insight into why you eat, you must stop for a moment and analyze your behavior; you may also wish to consult a professional. One thing that Glenda did which proved very useful was to keep a daily record of what she ate. I recommend that you do likewise. On the left side of the page, write down everything you eat — forbidden or not — along with the time and place; on the right side, mark down your reasons for eating. They may not come to you immediately, but persevere — there are always reasons why you eat.

Fleas at the ball park

Doris was an energetic young woman of 29 who worked as an office manager in an insurance company. She had recently completed a behavior modification course I was giving and had lost 30 pounds. Here's how she described a recent trip to the ball park.

"While reading the newspaper, between two food advertisements, I came across an ad for the local baseball team. As I had nothing else planned, I decided to take in a game. In the bus on the way to the stadium, I passed the time reading the ads posted in the bus. Whenever I glanced out the window, all I could see were these huge billboards for Kentucky Fried Chicken, Howard Johnson's, Macdonald's, and the like. The ads must have been effective, for each fast-food establishment we passed was jammed with people gorging themselves with hamburgers, French fries, soft drinks, and ice cream. At the stadium, it was even worse — a few players on the field plying their trade, and thousands of starved fans in the stands stuffing themselves with peanuts, popcorn, hot dogs, and beer. Forty thousand mouths chomping away. I'd say at least seven out of ten spectators were overweight. Unbelievable! But you know, the worst of it is, not too long ago I used to be exactly like those people at the ball park — and I wasn't even aware of it."

Doris just realized how she'd been brainwashed in the past; she'd been conditioned to eat without knowing it.

Each day, we're literally bombarded by stimuli tempting us, urging us to eat, eat, eat. We're so surrounded by these influences that we're no longer aware of them, but they affect us just the same. The secret of conditioning is repetition. Hit by the same message over and over again, we become zombies, robots programmed to eat. Only afterwards do we sometimes realize that we've stuffed ourselves even though we were no longer hungry.

Try the following experiment. Put some fleas in a jar and cover it. You'll notice that the fleas keep jumping to get out of the jar: they jump up, hit the lid, fall to the bottom of the jar, and jump up again. After a while, the fleas will continue jumping, but they'll no longer hit the cover. Even if you remove the lid, the fleas won't escape: by hitting their heads on the lid over and over again, the fleas learn not to jump so high, and they continue to jump lower even after the lid is removed. They become conditioned to act in a certain way and persist in their learned behavior even when it's no longer appropriate.

The fans at the ball park were like conditioned fleas. Shell-shocked from the media blitz urging them to eat, and caught in a verbal cross fire of vendors shouting: "Peanuts!" "Popcorn here!" "Chips! Chips!" they end up eating — withough even realizing it. Unlike fleas, though, we can become aware of our conditioning and "start jumping higher."

Doris saw the light and jumped out of the jar. When she looked at all the conditioned fleas at the ball park, she couldn't believe she used to be one of them.

Pavlov's dog

Our behavior is 90 percent conditioning. We learn to think, feel, and act automatically. For each experience we go through, our subconscious records our thoughts, emotions, and actions, so that when a similar situation occurs, we end up reacting in the same set way, without thinking.

A classic example of conditioning was provided by the scientist Pavlov, who conditioned a dog to salivate at the sound of a bell by ringing it just before presenting the animal with food. The procedure was repeated many times: first a bell was rung, then the dog was given something to eat. In this manner, the dog learned to associate the sound of the bell with food. Eventually, the dog responded to the bell by salivating even when food was no longer forthcoming. Try the experiment yourself; it takes anywhere from 4 to 21 days to train a dog in this way.

After I discussed Pavlov's experiment in one of my behavior courses, one of my patients, Janice, decided to try it out on her own dog. Although Rex was fed regular dog food, he had the habit of begging for table scraps, which Janice gladly gave him. The result: an overweight dog.

Not only can new habits be acquired through conditioning, but old ones can be lost as well, so for three weeks Janice refused to give Rex any leftovers despite his whining and begging. After just 12 days, the dog stopped coming to the dinner table for scraps; he no longer salivated when the family sat down for a meal, and was quite content with his daily ration of dog food. In a short time, Rex lost all his excess fat and became vigorous and alert again.

Coke and chips

Carla was a 52-year-old widow who worked as a saleslady in a department store. She loved cola, and was used to drinking six 24-ounce bottles a day. Her other habit was chips — but only on Fridays.

I explained to Carla that taste is a habit and that, with conditioning, she could lose her taste for any food in from 4 to 21 days. She first tried to kick the cola habit (she was already showing signs of diabetes from drinking too much of the beverage). After not touching a drop of cola for 18 days, she lost her craving for the drink — she no longer missed it. In fact, when she drank some cola a month later, it tasted funny to her. She thought it may have been a bad bottle, but when she asked some friends to try some, they all said it tasted normal. It was Carla's taste that had changed.

Strangely enough, it was getting rid of her potato chip habit that Carla found the most difficult, even though she was used to eating chips only once a week. Every Friday, she'd go through two jumbo-size bags of chips while watching the late night movie. You'd think she'd find it harder to kick the cola habit, for she drank cola every day, but Carla had it in her head that she absolutely had to have her chips on Friday night.

Human beings have an advantage over animals in that they can think, but sometimes this ability to think becomes a handicap. Carla didn't mind so much giving up cola — in fact, she was glad she did — because the drink was making her diabetic. But to her, eating chips on Friday night was a way of rewarding herself for working hard all week. After putting in her 35 hours, she felt she deserved to munch on chips if it helped her unwind. The only way Carla could shake the habit would be to change her way of thinking.

Chips were not really a good reward for Carla because they contributed to her obesity and her diabetes. And I doubt that chips have any intrinsic relaxant quality. Carla simply had to learn to reward herself and to relax another way. She did finally seek another outlet, and now spends her Friday evenings working out at a health club with her friend. She looks years younger and is in fantastic shape.

Summary

The conditioning of our thoughts, emotions, and behavior often prevents us from losing weight. The first thing we must do, therefore, is recognize how conditioning is affecting our lives. This can be quite difficult and may require the help of another person who can view our habits in a more objective way. No two people are conditioned in the same manner: we all think differently and have different habits and tastes.

Phoebe thought she was a glutton when, in fact, she was overeating to compensate for the frustration of living with an unaffectionate and inattentive husband. It was only 20 years later that she finally became aware of her habit. Gluttony doesn't exist — there are always reasons why we eat.

Glenda had a serious weight problem which she should have been able to solve. She couldn't though, because she thought it was normal for her to be obese. She hid herself in the house out of embarrassment and compensated for her boredom by eating, thus conditioning herself to associate boredom with food. She was caught in a vicious circle and thought there was no way out.

Doris finally realized she'd been conditioned to eat by all the advertisements around her, just as the fleas were conditioned by hitting their heads on the lid of the jar. Now, when she sees other people gorging themselves, she finds it hard to believe she used to be like them.

Carla kicked her cola habit in less than three weeks, but had trouble giving up her potato chip habit, even though she ate them only once a week. To her, chips represented a well-deserved reward after a hard week. In order to lose her taste for chips, she had to change her way of thinking, which she finally did.

If you overeat, you must find the reasons why and then try to change your way of thinking. If you put your mind to it, you can deprogram yourself in less than 21 days.

CHAPTER 13

HAPPINESS

Enjoying life

Sandi had been a patient of mine for about six years. Always cheerful and smiling, she weighed 242 pounds despite five or six diets. She would lose weight with incredible ease at the beginning of her diets, but after dropping about 30 pounds in six to eight weeks, she'd give up and gain back all the weight she lost. I'd always regarded Sandi as a happy person whose only problem seemed to be her obesity. Then one day she surprised me:

"What's the use of losing weight?" she asked me. "I might die in two weeks. Then I'd have punished myself for nothing. I want to enjoy life."

"Do you plan on dying in two weeks?"

"No, but who knows? Maybe it would be for the best."

"I've always known you to be a happy person — laughing, cracking jokes. Now you seem depressed . . ."

"I was never really happy — I just pretended to be. I've known my husband since I was 18 — he's the only man I've ever known. I went out with him for 13 years before marrying him."

"How old were you when you got married?"

"I was 31 and he was 39. We've been married for 10 years now — ten years of hell. He's forever criticizing me and yelling at me. He's never satisfied."

"That's surprising. I've met your husband several times and he seemed cheerful enough."

"I was surprised too. During the 13 years we were dating, he was completely different from the way he is now. As soon as we got married, he started to change. It seems he has a split personality."

"Thirteen years is a long time to date."

"I know. But he kept putting off the wedding for some reason or other."

"Why don't you have any children?"

"Had I been younger, perhaps I would've wanted kids, but my husband was against the idea. He said life's too difficult nowadays to bring children into the world."

"You trouble me a bit when you say that. It seems to me life's never been easier. Of course, everyone has problems, but that's normal. Never have people had so much opportunity to travel, to buy things, to indulge their every whim."

"We do take one or two vacations a year in the South, and we have a cottage on the lake where we go every weekend. We both work, so we can afford to spoil ourselves a bit."

"You have all that, and still you're not happy?"

"I've always worked, you see, and every paycheck I earn goes straight to my husband, but he doesn't appreciate it. All I get from his is criticism and complaints. Whenever he yells at me, I go into the kitchen and eat. It's my only consolation."

"If you were thinner, you'd have more energy and more stamina — you'd be able to enjoy all kinds of fulfilling activities which could add a little happiness to your life."

"Do you believe in happiness, Dr. Larocque?"

"I most certainly do. I think the key to happiness is within all of us. The problem is that people look for happiness outside themselves — they try to buy happiness. If you purchase a piece of furniture that you really like, it may give you pleasure for a while, but if you make a piece of furniture with your own two hands, you'll feel proud every time you look at it. It's not by purchasing things that we attain true happiness, but by doing things ourselves, by creating, by striving for what we want."

"I'd just as soon enjoy my life right now. You never know what the future may hold."

Sandi's only joy in life was food, and it would remain so until she learned to unlock the happiness inside her. She had everything she needed to succeed, to live a happy life. Buried within her was the most magnificent treasure on earth, the greatest power in the universe — but she didn't realize it. She was like a poor woman who spends her whole life in misery, only to discover on her deathbed that she had a huge fortune all along which she never used.

Sandi had a choice between the small pleasures in life and true happiness. She chose the small pleasures — in her case, eating — and obtained momentary satisfaction at the cost of obesity. She wanted to get the most out of life, but destroying her body wasn't the way to do it. Every year she got fatter and fatter, but she didn't seem any happier for it. Obesity is no way to enjoy life.

Nobody is born happy or unhappy. Happiness is a choice — it must be worked on and cultivated. So get cracking, and don't let anything or anybody stand in your way.

Learning to be happy

Terry was 51 years old and weighed 286 pounds. She was a domestic engineer, as she liked to put it. Since her blood pressure was high, I strongly suggested she lose weight so she could control her pressure without drugs. She wouldn't hear of it. "Don't talk to me about losing weight," she said. "I'd rather take pills."

Despite her attitude toward dieting, Terri was far from ignorant. In fact, she'd been a teacher for 15 years, but at the age of 36 she had to give up the profession she loved because of her sick husband. It was then that she started to gain her 170 pounds of excess weight. Her husband, a beer drinker who guzzled an average of 8 six-packs a day from the age of 27, was suffering from cirrhosis of the liver. For 15 years he vomited blood regularly, and at least once a month he had to be taken to the hospital where, each time, the doctors would evaluate his chances for survival. With blood transfusions and forced abstinence from alcohol, he somehow managed to scrape through.

Terri was having a rough time of it. Because of her alcoholic husband, she had to go on welfare. Then, as if that wasn't enough, her 26-year-old daughter left home after graduating from nursing school, leaving Terri feeling rejected. "I gave her everything," she fumed, "and that's the thanks I get." Unemployed, with a sick husband and a daughter who had rejected her, Terri felt as if she'd failed in every area of her life.

Terri's sole joy was eating, especially pecan pie. Since she couldn't find happiness within herself, she ate sweets as a way of compensating. The more unhappy she became, the more she relied on her pecan pie to pick her up.

Terri's problem was not insoluble, however. She couldn't draw her happiness from within, because she disliked herself for being such a failure. She thought she was a hopeless case who botched everything: her marriage, her family life, and her personal life. To attain true happiness, she had to learn to love herself again.

Loving yourself is not a sign of vanity or conceit — it's your moral duty. People who are full of themselves and who have a superiority complex don't like others and don't like themselves. They must continually knock others to prove their own worth, as if there weren't enough room at the top for everyone. In our society, people aren't taught to love themselves, lest they become vain or conceited. Often you'll hear people say: "Don't compliment her too much — it'll go to her head." But if we haven't learned to love ourselves, how can we love others? How can we be happy?

Success, like happiness, is a habit. Actually, Terri blew her failures out of proportion. Her unsatisfactory marriage was not her fault at all, but that of her irresponsible husband. As for her personal life, she deserved credit for assuming her moral responsibility toward the man she had married "for better or for worse." And, so far as her family life was concerned, she hadn't really been a failure at all. On the contrary, she'd been a continual source of inspiration for her daughter. That her daughter now wanted to leave home in order to stand on her own two feet was perfectly normal, and in no way signified rejection of her mother. "Yes, but she has no money," argued Terri. "I'd like to help her financially so she won't have to go through what I went through, but I don't have the money." If Terri couldn't be happy, she at least wanted her daughter to be. Like so many parents, she wanted to buy happiness for her child, but happiness is one thing money can't buy.

Making everything easy for your children is not the greatest gift you can give to them. You should instill in your children the desire to fight for what they want and to make whatever sacrifices are necessary to attain their goals. The greater the difficulties they overcome in reaching their goals, the more pride they'll feel, the more self-confidence they'll develop, the more they'll like themselves, and the happier they'll be.

When Terri mentioned to me that her daughter had this quality of fighting for what she wants, I told her it was the most precious gift she could have given her. But now it was time for Terri to set a goal for herself and to work hard to attain it. By striving to reach her goal, she'd learn to love herself more day by day, and she'd finally attain the happiness she deserved.

Learning to be happy wouldn't be easy for Terri, but she could do it if she set her mind to it. So can you.

Paying the price

A few months ago, I met a successful businessman at a party. Although in his sixties, he had a trim figure and exuded vitality and health. When we were introduced, I congratulated him on his appearance.

"Why, thank you," he replied. "Are you the Dr. Larocque who gives conferences and helps people lose weight? I thought you were much older."

"It's because I take good care of myself, just as you do."

"Well, I'd like to congratulate you for all you've done, and I hope you keep up the good work. There aren't enough people nowadays who are involved in prevention. Would you like to hear my story? I think it'll interest you."

"Go ahead, I'd love to hear it."

"I'm 63 years old. For two thirds of my life, I was obese — 88 pounds overweight. I drank more than my share of champagne, Scotch, and wine, and I ate too much for my own good, especially rich sauces. Being in the business world, I had plenty of opportunities to indulge myself. Businessmen's lunches from noon to 4 p.m., three or four times a week — you know the story. Every year, when I went to see my doctor, he'd say: 'Listen, Bill, you've got to do something. Sooner or later, you're going to pay the price. You already have diabetes and high blood pressure — don't wait till it's too late.' My answer was always the same: 'Not to worry. I take things one day at a time. If my number comes up, so be it — at least I will have enjoyed my life. I'm not one to regret things. I'm a businessman, and if I dwelled on all the mistakes I've made . . .' He'd reply: 'If you don't take the time to look after yourself now, you'll have to do it later, when you're seriously ill'.

"My doctor wasn't stupid — he knew what he was talking about. One morning — I was 42 years old at the time — I couldn't get out of bed. My whole right side was paralyzed. I couldn't move, I couldn't speak. I still remember, my wife was in the bathroom, and I tried to call her, but no words came out of my mouth. I felt as if I were suffocating. All this must have happened in a matter of minutes, but to me it seemed like an eternity. I was sure I was going to die. My whole life passed before my eyes. Suddenly, everything seemed so clear and simple to me. I realized then that I'd made my life more complicated than it really was. Then I had this sensation of leaving my body — I seemed to be floating above it. A calm, peaceful feeling came over me. No longer was I afraid. I remember my wife's reaction when she came out of the bathroom and found me unconscious. She let out a scream and started panicking. She kept talking to me — I could hear her, but I couldn't answer. Finally, I felt as if I were floating through this long, dark tunnel, moving closer and closer to the light at the end. Then, suddenly, I had a flash: I can't leave like this — there are too many things left for me to do.'

"I woke up four days later in intensive care. I'd just come out of coma. It was then that I learned that I'd suffered a heart attack and a stroke. I was lucky — I completely recovered from my paralysis in 10 days. Then the doctor gave me the news: 'Your heart's finished — there's nothing more we can do for you. You'd best go home to your family.' At the time, they didn't do heart operations like they do today. The doctor gave me no hope — I was condemned to await death quietly at home.

"I asked the doctor if there was anything I could do for myself. His reply: 'Lose your 88 pounds of fat, stop smoking — I was smoking 75 cigarettes a day —, don't overwork, and take up walking — gradually.'

"It was a tall order — exactly the opposite of what I'd done for 43 years. When I left the hospital, I was taking 10 nitros a day — I'd get chest pains if I exerted myself even the slightest bit. I was also taking a dozen other pills to strengthen my heart, to eliminate water, and to help me breathe and sleep.

"Believe it or not, six months later, stubborn mule that I am, I was no longer taking any pills. I'd lost my 88 pounds of fat, had given up smoking and drinking completely, and was jogging a mile and a quarter three times a week. It's been 20 years now and I've never been in better shape. I've gained back the years I threw away with all my foolishness. I'm too young to stop now."

His story over, I asked him: "Are you afraid of dying now?"

"Not in the least. Before my attack, deep down inside, I was scared of dying. But now I know death is nothing to be afraid of — it's a state of peace and calm.

Anyway, we all have to go sooner or later. In the meantime, I want to get the most out of life, to experience as much as I can. I want to live life to the hilt. It's when you lose your fears that you really start to appreciate life. My attack was the best thing that could've happened to me."

"But don't you think that having to watch what you eat and drink, and having to jog three times a week — at age 63 yet, — is a high price to pay?"

"You know, doc, if I've learned one thing in life, it's that the price of feeling good is never too high. It's our failures that we pay for."

"I agree with you completely — I just wanted to hear you say it."

"When I eat well, when I run, I feel good — I'm happy. If I skip my morning jog, I feel I'm missing something — I don't feel right. The same goes when I eat too much — I feel lousy and I hate myself for doing it. I enjoy everything I do to stay healthy. I don't consider it a chore — I enjoy it. In life, you pay only for your mistakes."

The only pleasure

Eve was a 31-year-old mother of two children aged 5 and 14. At the beginning of her diet, she weighed 381 pounds. When I asked her why she'd waited so long to lose weight, she answered, quite seriously, that there was only one pleasure in life: eating. She didn't mean it was *her* only pleasure, but that it was *the* only pleasure in life, for when I asked her if food was the only thing she enjoyed, she replied, "Of course not. I have a wonderful husband whom I love very much, and I adore my children — they're everything to me."

Even if there were other things in life that were meaningful to her, she still felt that eating was the only true joy in life. In fact, she was very content with her weight and wouldn't have come to see me had it not been for an unkind remark by her husband. She felt he complimented other women too frequently on the way they dressed and asked him why he never paid the same compliments to her. "You're too fat, that's why," he told her blankly. Eve was shocked. She didn't think 381 pounds was all that fat; after all, wasn't everyone always complimenting her on her figure? As she didn't have a full-length mirror at home, she went into the bathroom, removed her clothes, and stood up on the edge of the bathtub to take a good look at herself. It was true — she did have a roll of fat around the abdomen. Lately, she'd been complaining that chairs were too narrow for her and that they weren't as good as they used to be, and the previous week she had difficulty making it through the turnstiles in the subway. It was starting to dawn on her that perhaps she was fatter than she thought.

Eve wept all night long, not because she was too fat, but because her husband thought she was. She'd always been happy the way she was — why did she have to change?

Eve weighed 12 pounds at birth. Both her parents were obese and weighed more than twice their ideal weight. To them, a fat baby was a healthy baby. She was their first child, and they made sure she didn't want for anything, especially food. Firm believers in the saying "waste not, want not," they also saw to it that Eve finished everything on her plate, hungry or not. And there was always plenty of dessert — a meal without cake or pastry simply wasn't a meal.

Later, because Eve was fat for her age and couldn't participate in games her friends played, she became a T.V. addict. She's still one today — television is her only activity besides housework. All day long, the messages on T.V. reinforce what her parents taught her: to be happy, you have to eat. It was great to hear her favorite stars tell her that she had the key to happiness right in her refrigerator. Food certainly made her happy — what more proof did she need? She couldn't ask for anything more — after all, eating was *the* pleasure in life.

Eve came to see me every year in order to please her husband, and in so doing made herself unhappy for weeks and months. Her chances of succeeding were almost nil, and would remain so unless she became aware of her problem. She'd been brainwashed by her parents and, subsequently, by television, into believing that food was the only pleasure in life. She didn't want to give up her illusory happiness. Usually it takes a catastrophe, such as a separation or a serious illness, to wake up people like Eve. Unfortunately, when it happens, it's often too late.

Summary

The happiness-food mental block is easy to identify but difficult to overcome. Many people succomb to the influence of society and try to buy happiness rather than work for it.

Sandi didn't want to diet in case she had only a couple of weeks to live. She said she wanted to get the most out of life, but destroying and deforming her body with food wasn't the way to do it. Happiness must be learned and cultivated.

Terri could learn to love herself despite her hardships, but she had to be prepared to work for her goal, just as she'd taught her daughter to do. With each small victory, her confidence and self-esteem would grow. Happiness is a choice. You can't be happy if you don't love yourself.

Bill, a successful businessman, learned to live only after a close brush with death. He didn't consider his efforts to stay healthy a chore — he enjoyed working out and being fit.

Eve, 381 pounds, was under the illusion that eating is the key to happiness. Like an ostrich, she was hiding her head in the sand. I'm afraid she's in for a rude awakening.

Happiness can come only from within, from a sense of pride and accomplishment in having attained your goals through hard work. You can't buy happiness.

CHAPTER 14

SECONDARY GAIN

Lack of assertiveness

Eileen, 26, worked in a hospital as an auxiliary nurse. Barely 5 feet tall, she was 92 pounds overweight. From what she told me during her first visit, it was obvious she was suffering a great deal from her condition. She said she had nightmares in which her husband told her: "Don't worry, I'll have the door frames enlarged so you can get in and out of the house." Since I'd never had her as a patient before, I explained to her the two aspects of my therapy: weight reduction through dieting, and behavior modification — to treat the cause of the problem.

Eileen was very interested and registered immediately for my motivation and behavior courses. At the same time, she opted for a special 500-calorie diet with protein, vitamin, and mineral supplements. Her personality test revealed that she was a passive-aggressive type with a deep mistrust of others, strong guilt feelings, and an almost total lack of confidence and self-esteem.

In ten weeks, Eileen lost 35 pounds; not once did she cheat. When she took another personality test, the results indicated an almost normal subject with only a slight tendency towards aggression. Eileen's personality had undergone a complete metamorphosis: she was enthusiastic, energetic — a truly happy person.

When I asked Eileen if she knew the reason for her amazing transformation, she said it was nothing in particular; by simply attending my course, she'd become more aware of her importance — of her worth as a woman.

Throughout her entire life, Eileen had never made a decision on her own. At home, it was her authoritarian parents who decided everything. Then, at the age of 16, she met a young man five years older than her. After a few months of dating, he asked her to marry him. When she couldn't make up her mind, he told her not to worry — he'd discuss the matter with her parents. But her parents wouldn't hear of it — marriage was out of the question. So a compromise was made: Eileen would live together with her boyfriend, but under her parents' roof. This situation lasted for two years.

When Eileen turned 18, her boyfriend again broached the idea of marriage; he thought it time they had a place of their own. Eileen's parents agreed, and the wedding was arranged. As usual, Eileen had no say in the matter. She was just lucky he was a good husband.

Needless to say, Eileen's husband made all the decisions in their marriage. It was he who decided what food to buy, what movies to see, even what clothes Eileen should wear. Whenever he did ask her opinion, she could never make up her mind. Until the age of 26, she had never made a decision on her own.

The first time Eileen ever took the initiative in anything was when she came to see me in order to lose weight. It was her first step on the road to self-discovery. Finally, she began to unlock the vast potential within her which had remained untapped for 26 years.

As the weeks went by, Eileen learned to assert herself within her behavior group. Other people were interested in what she had to say, and they often felt the same way she did, so she no longer felt alone. Her self-esteem grew by leaps and bounds. In less than 10 weeks, she lost her feelings of jealousy and distrust that, in the past, had caused her to lose some of her best friends. No longer was she afraid of other women; she knew she was a worthwhile person in her own right.

For 26 years, Eileen had compensated for her lack of assertiveness by eating. Once she realized she could stand up for herself, she no longer felt the need to eat excessively. Now she makes all her decisions herself: *she* decided where to go on her vacation, and she also shared in the decision on what kind of family car to buy. She even picked out her own dress for the first time. Her husband was delighted. What a change! And talk about ambition — next year she wants to run in the Boston Marathon.

The woman who couldn't say no

Betty-Lou was in her forties. Very active socially, she was a member of numerous local clubs and organizations. Her 25 pounds of excess weight had been bothering her for several years: she tired too easily because of her extra pounds, and they made it difficult for her to maintain her busy schedule.

Betty-Lou's block was that she couldn't say no. She told me she'd recently been invited to her friend's home along with another companion. Her hostess had gone out of her way to prepare a delicious meal and had even bought a bottle of Betty-Lou's favorite wine. Upon tasting the wine, however, Betty-Lou realized that it had gone bad — it tasted like vinegar. Her friends didn't notice. It would have been a good opportunity not to drink any wine and to avoid needless calories, but Betty-Lou didn't want to disappoint her hostess. So she said nothing and forced herself to drink the sour wine, pretending to enjoy it. She even drank more than usual, almost finishing the whole bottle herself, because her other friend had a stomach problem and didn't want to drink too much for fear of aggravating her condition.

The following week, it was her grandmother's eighty-second birthday. A magnificent cake was served. Although Betty-Lou had vowed to lose weight and to avoid eating sweets, she ended up eating a large slice of her grandmother's birthday cake so as not to hurt her feelings.

Betty-Lou was a great organizer. One day, she invited me to give a conference at a women's club, to be followed by a buffet. While we were talking, a friend of hers joined us and said to her, "You don't drink in front of your doctor? Here, take this — you deserve it. You've organized a wonderful evening." Beaming with pride, Betty-Lou took the glass that was offered her. A few moments later, when we were alone again, she confided, "You know, I don't like drinking at all, and I realize it doesn't do my weight any good, but I can't say no. If I don't go along with everyone, they feel insulted — they think I'm snubbing them."

Betty-Lou's inability to say no was preventing her from losing weight. She couldn't refuse her friends anything for fear of losing their affection. She went out of her way to please others, but in so doing she wasn't being true to herself. She wasn't appreciated for who she was, but for someone who could be taken advantage of, who always said yes, who could always be counted on for a favor.

It's important to be helpful to others, but not at the expense of your own personality. To love and to be loved are admirable goals, but you should be loved for yourself, not for the favors you do.

Punishment

Madge, 38, was on her second diet. On her first, she managed to lose her 55 extra pounds, only to gain them back six months later. This time, she was well aware of the difficulties of maintaining her ideal weight and decided to enroll in my behavior and motivation courses once her diet was over.

It took Madge only four months to lose her 55 extra pounds again. Not once did she cheat on her diet. As soon as she started her maintenance diet, however, she went on an eating binge. "It was as if I'd just been let out of jail," she said. Madge now realized that she'd have to change her behavior and her way of thinking to avoid gaining back all the weight she'd lost.

After attending my courses for a few weeks, Madge told me she'd discovered one of the mental blocks that in the past had prevented her from maintaining her ideal weight:

"A couple of nights ago, as usual, I was waiting for my husband to come home from work. He was very helpful and supportive during my diet, and was very pleased that I lost weight — he didn't like fat women. To show my appreciation for all the encouragement he'd given me, I prepared his favorite dish. But that evening, he decided to go to the local bar after work with his buddies, so he got home an hour and a half late. I was furious. How could he do this to me? After all the trouble I'd taken to prepare his meal. After all the suffering I'd put up with to lose weight, just to please him. He was going to pay for this! I went to the pantry, ripped open a bag of cookies, and devoured them all. Luckily, I was taking your course at the time. The next morning, I sat down and began mulling over the events of the night before. Suddenly it hit me — I realized why I had gained back all the weight I lost on my first diet. I was angry with my husband, so to pay him back I ate like a pig for six months. It seems I can't control my emotions — I can't handle disappointment — so I compensate with food. I just eat and eat and eat."

Although Madge cheated on her diet, she used the incident as an opportunity to learn more about herself. Now that she had discovered her mental block, the future looked brighter to her.

"Did you feel guilty after eating all those cookies?" I asked her.

"Not at all. I could hardly believe what I'd done. It was like during my first diet — the more angry I'd get at my husband, the more I'd eat. Then I'd get mad at myself and eat even more. It was like that for six months. No, I didn't feel guilty. I just sat down the next morning and took a long, hard look at myself. I'm glad the whole thing happened — I feel I've taken a big step forward."

"When you have other disappointments and frustrations which have nothing to do with your husband, how do you react?"

"Well, just last week my sister-in-law left me in the lurch. We were supposed to go out together, but she changed her mind at the last moment. I was furious. I always do favors for her, but she never goes out of her way for me."

"Did you compensate for your disappointment by eating?"

"No, I went for a long walk. It seems when the problem's not with my husband, I get over it pretty quickly and I don't feel the urge to eat. Actually, now that I think of it, it's only when I'm mad at my husband that I can't control myself and I pig out."

When Madge raided the refrigerator after an argument with her husband, what she was doing in effect was punishing him. She knew he didn't like fat women, so whenever he upset her, she would eat to get even with him. Madge was caught in a vicious circle: she would eat to punish her husband, feel guilty about her behavior, and then eat even more to punish herself. Fortunately, she'd used her latest eating binge as an opportunity to understand herself better and had broken the vicious circle — she no longer felt guilty. Now, all she had to do was learn to control her emotions and frustrations with her husband as she did with other people.

Summary

As mentioned in Chapter 8, people with a psychological problem often try to cover up their hurt with obesity, instead of allowing it to heal naturally.

Eileen, till the age of 26, never made her own decisions, even when it came to getting married. To compensate for her lack of assertiveness, she ate excessively. After only 10 weeks of attending my behavior course, however, she underwent a complete transformation: she lost her feelings of jealousy and became a self-confident, proud young woman who was able to think for herself.

Betty-Lou, a highly active woman in her forties, was forever compromising herself to please others. She had an inordinate desire to be liked by everyone, so she never said no to anyone. What she had to realize was that people didn't like her for who she was, but because they could take advantage of her.

Madge was caught in a vicious circle: she would eat to punish her husband, feel guilty about her behavior, and then eat even more to punish herself. But after sitting down and taking a long, hard look at herself, she came to understand her problem and lost her guilt feelings. Now, all she had to do was learn to control herself with her husband as she did with others.

When the bandage on a wound causes it to fester, it's best to remove the bandage and let the wound heal naturally.

CHAPTER 15

IMITATION

Identification

Rosie was 27 years old and weighed 220 pounds, twice her ideal weight. She wanted to have a baby but couldn't get pregnant, even though she hadn't taken any precautionary measures for four years. So she consulted her gynecologist, who examined her thoroughly and had her undergo a battery of tests. No abnormalities were found. The gynecologist concluded that her sterility was due to obesity, and referred her to me.

Rosie came to my office accompagnied by her mother, who was also very obese and who seemed quite eager to have grandchildren. I explained the diet to them and said that Rosie's chances of becoming pregnant were pretty good if she lost enough weight. Since she seemed highly motivated, I thought she'd have no trouble losing the necessary pounds. I was wrong. After one month on her diet, Rosie lost only 5 pounds; she should have lost 15.

The diet monitor — a special device similar to a breathalyzer which uses a breath sample to determine the percentage of ketone bodies, or fat burnt in the blood — confirmed that Rosie was making little progress. Week after week, the results were discouraging — rather surprising for someone who wanted badly to lose weight so she could have a child. Rosie's mother, who came along each week, was also very disappointed by her daughter's failure to lose weight. When I asked Rosie why she thought she was having trouble on her diet, her answer was vague: "It seems I want to lose weight and I don't want to lose weight. I don't know what's the matter with me. One thing's for sure, though — I do want a child."

For her next appointment, I asked Rosie to come alone. Her mother wasn't upset at all and seemed to understand. She was willing to try anything for her daughter to get pregnant.

When Rosie came to see me a week later, alone, the results were no better. I tried to learn more about her and asked her questions about her husband, her sex life, her possible mental blocks, and her desire to lose weight, but nothing she told me could explain her failure to slim down.

"You seem quite close to your mother," I said.

"You're right — I'm very fond of her."

"But don't you find her presence suffocating at times?"

"Not at all. She always minds her own business. I'm the one who asks her to come with me."

"How does she get along with your husband?"

"Just great. He really likes her a lot, because she never meddles in our affairs. She comes over when we invite her and she never tells us what to do."

"And your father?"

"Well, that's a long story. My father was an alcoholic, and he used to beat my mother, my two sisters and me whenever he came home drunk at night. It got so bad, my mother had to get a divorce. I was five years old when they split up; my sisters were three and six. Although my father never sent my mother any money for child support, she never cried or complained. To make ends meet, she slaved six, seven days a week. During the day she worked as a maid, and at night she took in sewing. But we never wanted for anything. My mother's the most extraordinary person I know. When she starts something, she finishes it. She never gives up."

"Are you like your mother?"

"Are you kidding? I'm not half the woman she is, although I sure wish I were more like her." Rosie's eyes lit up when she spoke about her mother. To her, being like her mother was an impossible dream.

I was now beginning to understand why Rosie had so much trouble losing weight. I explained my theory to her:

"I don't think you really want to lose weight to be slimmer."

"You're right. I'm quite content at my present weight. I just want to get pregnant."

"The reason you accept your obesity is that you want to be like your mother, who seems to be a marvelous woman but who also happens to be very obese."

"Perhaps."

"You have a lot of confidence in your mother, much more than you have in yourself."

"True."

"And by losing weight, you'd lose your identification with your mother and, with it, all your self-confidence. You'd feel all alone."

"I'm not sure that's exactly how it is, but it's an interesting theory. It's true that I want to be like my mother and that I depend on her a lot."

"We're going to try an experiment. We're going to try to persuade your mother to lose weight at the same time as you. It wouldn't do her any harm, and we'll see if my theory's right."

"Okay, if that's what you want."

After explaining my plan to Rosie's mother, she was more than willing to cooperate. So mother and daughter both went on the same protein diet. In 10 weeks, Rosie's mother lost 29 pounds, while Rosie shed 31 (in addition to the 5 pounds she'd already lost). Rosie had to discontinue her diet during the eleventh week, because she stopped menstruating. A week later, she took a pregnancy test; the result was positive.

Rosie had reached her goal of becoming pregnant, but she still had plenty of work to do to become independent. There was nothing wrong with admiring her mother, but she had to develop her own self-confidence, her own identity.

Each of us is a unique human being. We must learn to accept ourselves as we are, with our good points and bad. It's fine to think highly of someone else and to try to emulate them, but we can never be someone else. To deny our true selves is self-destructive.

Visualization

Kristin was 86 pounds overweight. She had tried several times to lose weight, but her heart was never really in it. Whenever her blood pressure rose above 200/100, she'd suffer terrible headaches and would have to lose about 20 pounds to lower her pressure and ease the pain.

Kristin's mental block was most interesting. She'd always known that her mother had never loved her, and was deeply hurt by this. Her mother had desperately wanted a boy, so when she gave birth to a girl — Kristin — she was greatly disappointed and took it out on her daughter. Even at age 82, her mother still harbored a grudge against her.

At the age of four, Kristin was sent off to live with her grandmother so that her mother could return to her job as cocktail waitress. Her grandmother was an extraordinary woman who did everything she could to give Kristin the affection she needed. Needless to say, Kristin was very fond of her grandmother; it was as if she were her real mother. When I asked her what image she had of her grandmother, she told me she saw her sitting in her rocking chair in the corner of the kitchen, with her white apron, her red polka dot dress, and her grey hair. When I asked her if she wanted to be like her grandmother, her eyes lit up.

"Would I ever!" she replied. "She was an extraordinary woman."

"You haven't mentioned anything about her weight."

"She was rather fat. Actually, I look a lot like her."

So attached was Kristin to her grandmother that when she passed away, Kristin felt as if a part of herself had died. Years later, she still hadn't gotten over her grandmother's death.

Because Kristin felt rejected from a very early age by her mother, she considered herself worthless. The only person who really cared for her and loved her was her grandmother, whom she idolized. Her grandmother became a model for her, someone to imitate, for she possessed all the qualities Kristin admired and wished she herself had.

The danger in trying to emulate people we admire is that in trying to *be* like them, we often try to *look* like them, In Kristin's case, since the person she idolized was her grandmother, I suggested she imagine her grandmother slimmer and that she find a photo of her that way.

Summary

People who have a tendency to identify with or imitate others usually have a poor self-image. They lack confidence and self-esteem and try to compensate for these deficiencies by modeling themselves after someone they admire.

In the following chapters, we shall examine how our self-image affects us and how to improve it.

Imitation-type mental blocks, while not very frequent, can still cause problems if not correctly diagnosed. Rosie's identification with her mother was so strong that her mother had to go on a diet with her in order for her to lose weight. In Kristin's case, it was her obese grandmother who was idealized; in trying to be like her, Kristin ended up looking like her. To solve her problem, she had to imagine her grandmother slimmer. More important, she had to learn to be herself and to exploit her full potential, something she'd never done before.

In fifteen years of medical practice, I've never seen a patient who didn't have more good qualities than bad. Unfortunately, most people are unaware of their good points. If you want to be successful, you must be yourself and accept yourself.

CHAPTER 16

SELF-PUNISHMENT

Sex and drugs

Joy, 49, was the type of woman who stands out in a crowd. She was 5 feet 9 inches tall, weighed 165 pounds, and had an irresistable smile. Highly active, she attended evening courses at university to broaden her horizons and was a member of numerous local organizations. She was liked by everyone, and was looked upon as someone who always succeeded.

Joy was coming to see me for the second time. Eight months earlier, she had gone on a diet but had given up after only a few weeks. This failure embarrassed her greatly, and she had to swallow her pride to come and see me again. This time, to improve her chances of success, she decided to take my behavior and motivation course while following her diet.

The first few weeks went very well. During her tenth class, Joy made an interesting remark: "What strikes me the most so far is how simple our problems are when we get to know ourselves better. I used to look for all kinds of complicated explanations for my obesity, but it was all in my head. I can't believe I'm finally going to solve my problem. I'm going to be slim and beautiful.''

The following week, Joy didn't show up for her class; she left a message with my secretary saying she couldn't continue the program. Not understanding why she'd dropped out, I called her personally and asked her to come and see me. I explained to her that we'd already gotten to the heart of her problem, and that it was probably a psychological block that was causing her to give up when success was within her grasp. If we could identify her block, it would then be a simple matter to eliminate it, and her success would be assured.

Although Joy came to see me, she was still intent on quitting.

``I wish you could explain to me why you want to give up,'' I said. ``Just last week, you thought your problem was simple and that you were on the road to success. Were you mistaken then?''

``Not at all. I see my problem very clearly now and I sincerely believe I could succeed, but I don't deserve to. It's funny, everyone thinks I'm a great success, except me. Nothing I do gives me any real satisfaction. I'm a worthless person who doesn't deserve anything.''

``It seems to me you're trying to belittle yourself — perhaps even punish yourself.''

``You're probably right, and I deserve it.''

``But why punish yourself so?''

``My whole life's a disaster. I'm good for nothing. Four months ago, my 29-year-old son committed suicide — he took an overdose of heroin. I couldn't even make my own son happy — I couldn't even help him. I got this strange phone call from him the day before he took his life — he told me he loved me very much and that it wasn't my fault he had drug problems. He said it would be over soon, and that I wouldn't have to worry about him any more. I didn't even catch on that he was saying his last good-bye, that he'd decided to kill himself. Had I understood, I could have changed his mind, brought him to his senses. But no, I couldn't even hear his cry of despair. It's all my fault. I should have died instead of him."

Like many parents whose children commit suicide, Joy felt guilty for her son's death. She wondered where she had gone wrong. I explained to her that I understood her guilt feelings, but that they were probably unjustified, and that she was hurting herself for nothing. I told her we would discuss the matter at greater length in future sessions, to help her get rid of her painful feelings.

During our subsequent talks, I learned that Joy had been a good mother to her son, that she'd given him all the attention and affection he needed, and that she'd done everything in her power to make him happy. Nevertheless, Joy was still racked by guilt.

Then, one day, she made the following confession:

"There's something else I've never mentioned to you — I'm a nymphomaniac. I've been married for 21 years, and for the last 16 years I've had a lover whom I don't even care for. I love my husband and I'm very happy with him, but when I think of my lover, I get a tingling sensation in my vagina and I feel an irresistable urge to make love with him. I usually end up going to his place for sex about two afternoons a week. But I don't love him. In fact, each time I see him I tell him it's my last visit, that I won't be coming back. But I always do. I can't help it — I've been having sex with him for 16 years now, and I can't live without it."

I finally knew the real cause of Joy's guilt feelings. Now I had to find out the reasons behind her extramarital affair.

Joy truly loved her husband and was filled with remorse for being unfaithful. He didn't know about her illicit carryings-on, so he wasn't hurt by them. It was Joy who was suffering, week after week. Although her affair was tearing her up inside, she was unable to break it off — she couldn't help herself. It was only after several months of therapy that Joy came to understand her sexual behavior.

Raised by nuns till the age of 18, Joy had a very strict upbringing. When she confessed one day to having masturbated, she was severely reprimanded and ordered to cease her disgusting habit immediately, lest she turn into some kind of a pervert. Although she wanted to stop masturbating, the habit persisted, so she concluded that she must be abnormal. The vicious circle had begun: thinking herself abnormal, she then opted for an abnormal sex life, thus proving to herself that there really was something wrong with her.

By repeating to herself over and over again that she was a nymphomaniac, she ended up believing it and acting the part. Our thoughts determine our actions.

Once Joy understood the reasons for her behavior, her guilt feelings vanished. She then learned to program herself positively by focusing on her successes and her strong points. Her self-esteem grew rapidly, and it wasn't long before she lost her excess weight. Her marriage is now stronger than ever, and she enjoys a healthy and fulfilling sex life with her husband.

Separation

Anita, the fifth in a family of eight children, married at the age of 18. Nine years later, with three young children of her own, she separated from her husband. Although he was a lazy drunkard who ran around with other women, Anita's parents couldn't accept the fact that she'd separated from him. They were deeply religious and believed that when you married someone, it was for better and for worse. So upset were they with their daughter that they wouldn't even allow her to set foot in their house. Anita was crushed. Not only had her marriage failed, but she'd been rejected by her own family. A short while later, she suffered a nervous breakdown.

Anita was 49 years old when she came to see me. Still haunted by feelings of guilt over her separation, she'd become a very negative person, full of gloomy thoughts. She was afraid of everything and had no self-confidence. Although she did a pretty good job of bringing up her three children, she kept blaming herself for the fact that they had no father. Whenever something went wrong, she would say to herself: "It's God's way of punishing me for what I did to my children."

Anita was 44 pounds overweight; on her wedding day, she weighed only 110. In her mind, her obesity and her dark thoughts were normal punishments for separating from her husband and leaving her three children fatherless. Even though the breakup of her marriage had occured 20 years ago, she was still racked by guilt. Such feelings can often last a lifetime.

When Anita asked me if she was wrong to have split with her husband, I told her she had done the right thing. She made the best of a bad situation by leaving her irresponsible husband. She didn't dump him for a lover; she left him because it was the best thing for herself and her three children. It was only because her parents had judged her too harshly that she'd spent the last 20 years of her life torn by feelings of inadequacy and guilt.

Anita had to change her way of thinking, but it was not something that could be done overnight. She had to reevaluate her separation and analyze the last 20 years of her life to see who was responsible for what. Was she to blame for such and such an occurrence, or was it her ex-husband or her parents who were at fault?

Anita also had to put an end to her gloomy thoughts once and for all. To do this, she employed the STOP technique. This technique consists in saying the word "stop" to yourself, or even out loud, while at the same time forming an image of the word "stop" in your mind, whenever you start thinking negative thoughts. Then you immediately replace these dark thoughts with positive ones, such as imagining yourself in a situation you've always dreamed of, happy and relaxed. Anita pictured herself having a wonderful time at the beach with her three children.

If you believe your dreams strongly enough, they often come true. Anita's did: her children invited her to vacation with them at a seaside resort the following summer.

Prostitute

Mandy was 5 feet tall and weighed 260 pounds. She had already tried all kinds of diets, but nothing seemed to work. One time, while under my supervision, she managed to lose 55 pounds, but then she suddenly quit for no apparent reason. This time, I questioned her at length on the reasons for her previous failures.

"When I see myself getting thinner, something comes over me. I break down and I start crying for days on end. I feel better only when I start putting on weight again. I feel guilty for cheating on my diet, but I continue to eat in order to punish myself — it seems I enjoy punishing myself."

As soon as Mandy began slimming down, as soon as she could see some positive results of which she could be proud, as soon as people began complimenting her on her improved appearance, she broke down and began weeping, as if she weren't entitled to succeed. Why the feelings of guilt? Why the need to punish herself? Obviously, there was something in her past that was bothering her.

Mandy started to put on weight when she was seven years old. It was also at that age that she began having sexual relations with a 60-year-old man. He was a neighbor and friend of the family who baby-sat for her two or three times a week while her mother was away at work. The relationship, which included petting, masturbation, and penetration, went on for 10 years. At the time, Mandy's feelings about the situation were mixed: on the one hand, she enjoyed the attention and affection the man gave her; on the other, she felt guilty about doing something she knew was abnormal.

In order to punish herself, Mandy tried to deform her body by putting on weight. She also thought that if she were fatter, the man might find her less attractive and leave her alone. She wasn't strong enough to break off the relationship herself. Another thought bothered her as well: the man had made a habit of slipping a quarter under her pillow after each encounter; although she appreciated the money, she began to wonder if she was turning into a prostitute.

At the age of 18, she married a man her own age who was extremely kind and loving. However, because she'd previously received money for engaging in sex, she thought of herself as a whore who was unworthy of such a fine husband. After about a year, she confessed the whole story to her husband in the hope that he would throw her out, which was all she felt she deserved. But he didn't. Instead, he was very understanding and offered to help her as much as he could. This only made her feel more guilty: she had the most wonderful husband in the world, but she didn't deserve him.

Although she was a loving mother to her children — she even made all of their clothes by hand — Mandy considered herself a worthless person. When she began to see some positive results with her diet, she broke down, unable to accept success. In her mind, she deserved to be punished for the rest of her life.

Mandy had to learn to accept her past and to look at it in a more realistic way. She had been seduced by a 60-year-old man who had given her the affection and attention she wasn't getting from her parents. This did not make her a prostitute. It was wrong for her to keep blaming herself, for a 7-year-old could not be held fully responsible for her actions. It was the sick old man who was guilty of taking advantage of a young girl's innocence.

Mandy had to rid herself of her suicidal guilt feelings which were preventing her from living a normal life. She no longer had any reason to punish herself. It was time for her to develop her full potential, to make the most of her life, so that she could live happily and bring happiness to those she loved. She owed it to herself.

Unwanted child

Betty-Sue was 44 years old. When she first came to see me, she weighed 225 pounds, but after six months of dieting, she got her weight down to 140 pounds, just 5 pounds above her ideal weight. Although she occasionally cheated on her diet, I showed her how to learn from her mistakes to improve herself. Each time she cheated, she gained further insight into herself and was able to identify the habits she had to change. She was building a solid foundation for herself. I was very pleased with her progress and encouraged her to keep up the good work. Then, one day, the unexpected occurred. She marched into my office and tossed on my desk the daily diet record I had asked her to keep.

"Here, take a look at this," she said. "Usually, you're pleased when I cheat on my diet, because you say it can be taken in a positive way. Well, you're going to be in seventh heaven now."

Betty-Sue had cheated all week long, for no apparent reason. It was the first time she'd ever done that.

"I'll never be able to maintain my weight," she said tearfully. "I cheated all week. You're just wasting your time with me — I'm a lost cause."

Betty-Sue's behavior was surprising, to say the least. For six months, she'd been so positive, so enthusiastic; now, all she could talk about was how rotten she was. From the way she was putting herself down, it was obvious she was harboring some deep guilt feelings about something, and I had to find out what it was.

"How did you get along with your parents?" I asked.

"Not very well, but I'd rather not talk about it. Anyway, it has nothing to do with my weight problem."

I explained to her that our relationship with our parents often plays a key role in how we see ourselves. Our parents have a large impact on our lives — for better or for worse — because when we're young we believe everything they say.

Betty-Sue couldn't talk about her parents. She mumbled something about having a mental block, then burst into tears. Patiently, I asked her some simple questions to which she could reply by simply nodding her head. She slowly began to unblock. With a little more prodding, she finally admitted that she'd been an unwanted child. Her mother, while carrying her, wanted to have an abortion, but in those days it wasn't possible. So she consoled herself in the hope that she'd have a boy — she already had two girls. When she gave birth to Betty-Sue, she became very bitter and blamed the baby for upsetting her plans. Over and over again, she told Betty-Sue that she was unwanted, and that the only reason she was conceived was that her father was drunk at the time.

Betty-Sue's father was a violent alcoholic. She recalled being beaten by him at the age of five and having bruises all over her body for several weeks. A few years later, her father walked out on the family. His place was taken by a succession of male friends of her mother, none of whom stayed for more than a few weeks. All the while, Betty-Sue's mother kept blaming her for being born and for spoiling her plans. Even today, at the age of 80, her mother criticizes her whenever she sees her and tries to make her feel guilty.

It was hardly surprising, then, that Betty-Sue felt worthless — after all, even her own mother had rejected her. She couldn't understand how her husband could be satisfied with her either and often told him he could easily find someone better than she. Her low self-esteem also explained why she'd given up her diet just as she was getting down to her ideal weight: she felt she didn't deserve to succeed.

Of course, it was not Betty-Sue's fault she was an unwanted child. Furthermore, the fact that her father was drunk at the time she was conceived had nothing whatsoever to do with the quality of his sperm. Many great men and women have been born to alcoholic parents, so Betty-Sue had nothing to worry about in that regard.

Once Betty-Sue realized that her guilt feelings were unfounded, she regained her enthusiasm and her positive outlook on life. Losing her last five pounds of fat was then a cinch.

Summary

Self-punishment is a serious block: not only can it result in obesity, but it can poison an entire life. Often persisting for many years, it is an irrational, self-defeating kind of behavior. We can be responsible for our actions and bear the consequences without burdening ourselves with needless guilt. Although we're not perfect, we can improve ourselves by learning to accept our mistakes and benefit from them. It's also important that we not feel guilty for other peoples' errors.

Joy felt guilty for her son's suicide and especially for being a nymphomaniac. Because she had engaged in a sexual activity which she had been led to believe was deviant, she considered herself abnormal and acted as if she really were.

Anita felt guilty for separating from her unfaithful, alcoholic husband, because her parents rejected her for having broken her marriage vows. Whenever something went wrong in her life, she thought God was punishing her for leaving her children fatherless. She ignored the fact that she had been an excellent mother and that leaving her husband was the best thing she could have done under the circumstances. By deprogramming herself with the STOP technique, she was able to eliminate in a few months the guilt feelings that had been torturing her for 20 years. Now she can live a normal life again.

Mandy felt guilty, from the age of seven, for having had sexual relations with a 60-year-old man. Because he slipped a quarter under her pillow after each encounter, she considered herself a prostitute and tried to punish herself by becoming grossly overweight. Mandy had to stop feeling guilty about past events for which she was not to blame. She had to accept the past and make the most of the present and future. She owed it to herself to be happy.

Betty-Sue felt guilty for being an unwanted child whose father was an alcoholic. For 44 years, she'd been blaming herself for something over which she'd had no control. Once she realized her guilt was unfounded, she stopped denying herself the success and happiness she deserved.

Guilt is a negative, destructive emotion. To eliminate guilt feelings, it is important to identify the reasons behind them. No mistake is worth destroying an entire life.

CHAPTER 17

EMOTIONAL SHOCK

Perfectionist

A while ago, a childhood friend of mine called to ask me if I could see his wife. Caroline was 30 pounds overweight, but had never consulted a doctor for her weight problem, She had tried several diets on her own, without success. I agreed to see her the following week.

Caroline was a charming woman who worked as a secretary for a large company. She had no children. When I asked her why she wanted to lose weight, she told me she really didn't want to. It was her husband's idea that she come and see me.

"When he married me," she said, "I was already fat, but he didn't mind. Neither of us wanted children at the time. But when he turned thirty recently, he changed his mind and decided he'd like to have a child. That's why he wants me to lose weight. But I haven't changed my mind — I don't want any children and I'm not interested in losing weight."

"Why don't you want children?"

"I love them too much. Life's so hard and people are so messed up nowadays that I can't see myself bringing a child into this world — I couldn't bear to see him suffer. Two couples we know both have problems with their kids. One boy's seeing a psychologist, another's suffering from asthma. There's so much pollution in the air, I can't imagine my child breathing such poison. And with the economy the way it is, I'm not sure I could give my child everything he needs. No, I just don't think it's a good idea to have kids nowadays."

"It seems to me you're afraid of having children because you're not sure how they'll turn out."

"You're right. I never start anything unless I'm sure I'm going to succeed. I'm a perfectionist."

"But aren't you depriving yourself of a lot of interesting experiences?"

"I'm happy enough the way I am. I don't need anything more."

While trying to find out why Caroline avoided any endeavour that entailed even the slightest risk of failure, I learned that she was an only child whose father died when she was two. Her mother, a dressmaker, worked day and night so Caroline could go to school and become a teacher, something she herself and always wanted to be but hadn't been able to. She put a lot of pressure on Caroline to succeed, and her daughter responded by studying very hard: she loved her mother dearly and would do anything to make her happy.

Unfortunately, Caroline failed her exams and was unable to attend teacher's college. Her mother's dreams were dashed; Caroline was devastated. It wasn't so much not being a teacher that upset her; rather it was having failed after working so hard and, especially, having disappointed her mother. From that day on, she vowed never again to get involved in anything unless she was sure of succeeding. And she kept her word, too. Here we were, 10 years later, and she didn't want to have a child unless she was able to make him happy. She also didn't want to start a diet for fear of failing. After all, she knew so many people who gained back the weight they lost. By avoiding risks, she avoided disappointing herself and others. But her life was so much the poorer. Her motto, "give me perfection, or give me nothing," was causing her to lead a dull existence.

Caroline suffered an emotional shock when she failed her college entrance exams. This shock triggered a mental block that was affecting her entire life. Rather than seeking challenges and living an exciting life, she played it safe and engaged in only those activities where she knew she could do well.

To be happy, you must have goals. Of course, you will fail at one time or another — everybody does — but that's no reason to give up. Instead, you should learn from your failures to improve your chances of succeeding next time. It's by struggling to reach your goals that you'll attain true happiness. Nothing comes easy, but if you keep plugging away, you'll make it — if not this time, then the next.

Caroline had the right to fail her exams, but it was wrong for her to remain paralyzed by perfectionism for the rest of her life. We all realize that perfection doesn't exist and that nobody's perfect, but when it comes to ourselves, it's often a different story. We find it difficult to accept our mistakes and our failures. Instead of blaming ourselves when we foul up, we should realize that to err is human and try to learn from our mistakes.

A friend of mine who went bankrupt at the age of 38 put it very well when he said: "I hope this setback doesn't affect me so much that I'll be afraid to try other ventures in the future. That would be the worst thing that could happen to me."

Catastrophe

Cheryl, 24, was 5 feet 2 inches tall and weighed 282 pounds. A former patient of mine whom I'd known for about five years, she had tried every diet imaginable, but hadn't been able to lose any weight. This time, she was determined to succeed.

Before she began her new diet, I asked Cheryl to think about the goals she hoped to attain by losing weight and to jot them down. When she returned the following week, she handed me a sheet on which she'd written the following: "My goal is to get married and have two children. I can already see myself at the beach in a sexy bikini, romping with my husband and my two little ones."

With her goals clearly established, Cheryl eagerly started her diet. Never before had I seen her so motivated and so enthusiastic. Week after week, the pounds just melted away. It was obvious she had overcome a mental block of some kind; I asked her if she knew what it was.

"I think I do," she replied. "I started to put on weight at the age of five, when my parents separated. I never saw my father again after the separation, and I thought it was just terrible. I couldn't accept not having a father. Whenever I was with my friends, I'd ask them all about their fathers and tell them how horrible it was not to have one. Even as an adult, I still missed my father. I used to date older men, guys twice my age. When I was 16, I suffered my first broken heart: my 32-year-old boyfriend left me, just as my father had years earlier. I cried for six months. It was a catastrophe, a terrible catastrophe. I kept reliving the experience, over and over.

"Whenever I started a diet, it was with little conviction. I thought it was terrible to be deprived of food, and I always gave up after a few weeks. I had to do without my father — I had no choice — but why should I have to do without food? Why couldn't I eat like everyone else? Each time I quit a diet, I said to myself: 'If only my father were here, he'd know how to encourage me to stick it out.'

"It was only recently that I got over this mental block of mine. By analyzing myself and reading up on the subject, I realized that I'd been deeply affected by the loss of my father and had never really accepted it. I needed him desperately but he wasn't there. I kept thinking how catastrophic it was that I had no father. But now I realize that although it would have been preferable had my father remained with the family, I can still live normally without him. There's no point spending my whole life feeling sorry about something that can't be changed. Now I'm not so uptight. I accept that things can't always be the way I'd like them to be, and I feel much better. I live and let live."

Cheryl learned to control her destructive emotions by changing her way of thinking. She learned to live and let live, to accept what couldn't be changed. She learned to remove from her vocabulary words like terrible, horrible, catastrophic, always and never. It was by repeating these words over and over again that she developed the habit of overeating whenever she suffered a minor setback. Now Cheryl repeats to herself: "Live and let live." And it works.

Rejection

The day after one of my conferences, a 40-year-old secretary came to my office for a consultation. She weighed 226 pounds.

"I'd heard about you and I attended your conference yesterday," she said. "I think you're the doctor for me. I have to lose all my extra weight and I need your help to do it. Right now I'm highly motivated, so there shouldn't be any problem, but I'm also very emotional — I hope you won't drop me when I need you."

"I'm not in the habit of dropping my patients," I replied. "I'll help you as best I can."

Appointments were set up, and Kim began her diet. For the first three months, everything went smoothly. Kim was an energetic woman brimming with self-confidence. Each week, though, she would leave the office with the same words: "I'm very emotional, so please don't drop me."

One day, Kim showed up for her appointment looking as if she'd just been to a funeral.

"I told you I was very emotional," she said. "You won't drop me, will you?"

"Is something the matter?"

"One of my best friends just dropped me."

"Why? Did you have an argument?"

"No, it's not that. You see, a few months ago, she became a Jehovah's Witness, and now she's not allowed to associate with non-believers. I didn't want to convert to her new religion, so she had to drop me as a friend. It was either me or her religion, and she chose her religion."

"It was probably a difficult choice for her to make. I don't think she rejected you, though, or that she has anything against you. It's just that her religious beliefs took precedence over her personal feelings. I can understand your feeling disappointed, but you're acting as if it's the end of the world."

"I warned you that I was very emotional. When my friend told me she had to choose between me and her religion and that she'd chosen her religion, I suffered the same shock as when my mother placed me in boarding school at the age of seven.''

''Why did your mother send you to boarding school?''

''She was too busy to take care of me. My father died shortly after I was born, and my mother took over his business. She hired a nursemaid to look after me, but I was too hyper — she couldn't handle me. So my mother sent me off to a boarding school. I felt just awful — imagine being rejected by your own mother! She used to visit me once a week and bring me chocolate, probably to ease her conscience. But I knew she didn't love me. During my first month at the school, I sulked all the time and refused to eat or participate in any activities. Finally, I had no choice but to go along. It was then that I started to put on weight. I think it was my way of compensating for the affection I wasn't getting from my mother. Besides, I'd been brought up to believe that you should always finish what's on your plate.''

''I remained at the school until I was 18. When I left, I weighed 176 pounds. Shortly thereafter, I met a man. We got married a year later, after discovering that I was pregnant. Before the baby was born, though, my husband left me — no warning, no explanation. I never saw him again. I felt the same way as I had at the boarding school — rejected. I never really loved my husbanb, but I needed to be loved. After he left me, I went through a severe depression. I came out of it when my child was born. He was such a wonderful boy, he made me feel like living again. But to this day, I'm still very emotional. As soon as I see that I'm not loved or appreciated, I feel rejected and start eating.''

Kim was a very stable woman who had only one weakness: she couldn't tolerate the idea of not being loved. When she was placed in a boarding school at the age of 7, she felt terrible because she thought her mother didn't love her. When her marriage failed, it was the same story, only this time it was her husband who didn't love her. Now, as soon as she feels rejected by someone, she acts as if it's the end of the world.

To control her emotions, Kim had to learn to think differently. She had to say to herself: "It would be preferable if my mother, my husband, my friend, and everyone else loved me, but they have the right not to. I can't force them to love me."

Summary

Whenever we suffer an emotional shock, we end up reacting the same way to any situation similar to that which triggered the original shock. Even when the original incident is long forgotten, we continue to over-react whenever a like incident occurs. Our reaction becomes automatic.

Caroline suffered a terrible shock when she failed her exams and thus developed a fear of failure which continued to haunt her years later. Paralyzed by perfectionism, she steadfastly refused to try anything unless she was sure of succeeding. This negative attitude prevented her from having children and losing weight. Because she always played it safe, Caroline never knew the happiness that comes from accepting new challenges.

Cheryl discovered her emotional block all by herself and learned to control the automatic responses associated with it. The loss of her father was no longer viewed as a catastrophe, but as an unfortunate event that couldn't be changed. Gradually, she learned to live and let live. She learned that nothing is catastrophic, that there are simply pleasant things and unpleasant things, and that it was up to her to make the most of them. She couldn't let every small setback spoil her happiness.

Kim was placed in a boarding school at the age of 7 and felt terrible about it because she thought her mother had rejected her. From then on, she was unable to handle any kind of rejection. To overcome her emotional block, she had to accept the fact that she couldn't be loved by everyone and that she couldn't force anyone to love her.

CHAPTER 18

REACTION

Obligation

Loretta was a 58-year-old widow with a serious heart problem. She had suffered a heart attack six years earlier and now showed symptoms of angina upon exertion. At 5 feet 1 inch and 255 pounds, she was considerably overweight. Six months before she came to see me, her cardiologist had declared her unfit for work and told her bluntly that she had only six months to live if she didn't lose weight.

Not wanting to die, Loretta came to see me determined to slim down. She lost 60 pounds in short order and began to feel much better: her angina pains almost vanished and she was able to breath much easier. Once again, she was able to do her own errands and take care of the housework.

Everything was going well, her electrocardiogram was improving, when suddenly, Loretta stopped losing weight. For four or five days a week she would stick to her diet, but on the other days she would stuff herself with donuts, ice cream, and chocolate.

Week after week, I tried to motivate her. I asked her to find a photo of herself when she was very obese and to write on the back all the disadvantages of being overweight. She came up with the following: angina, shortness of breath, inability to work, fatigue, low self-esteem. I also asked her to jot down all the advantages she would derive from being at her ideal weight. Her list ran as follows: more energy, more stamina, ability to take care of herself, greater self-esteem. Although Loretta was clearly aware of both the drawbacks of remaining obese and the benefits of slimming down, she still could not maintain her diet for more than four or five days a week.

After delving into her past a bit, I learned that she'd always been very independant; she didn't like to be told what to do.

"I've never been able to take orders from anyone, even at work," she explained. In fact, I once quit my job for that reason. I told myself that if they weren't happy with my work, they could find someone else, and I left."

"You seem rather headstrong . . ."

"You're right, I am quite headstrong. I got it from my father, who was very authoritarian. When I was 16, he beat me once because I came home 15 minutes late. Actually, I started to become unruly when I was 12. One evening, my mother went out and my father stayed home to look after me. I was lying in bed when he came up to my room and asked me to take my clothes off. He started playing with my body, and then he took his penis out. He wanted to rape me, but I ran out of the house. Before then, I'd always been easy to get along with, but after that incident I refused to take any more orders from my father, or from anyone else for that matter. As soon as someone asks me to do something, I get very suspicious — I think they have ulterior motives and that they want to do something bad to me."

Loretta's father committed suicide at the age of 60, but the damage had already been done to his daughter. Any time she was obliged to do something, she would recall the unfortunate incident with her father and would react violently. Thus, when the cardiologist told Loretta that she *had* to lose weight, she refused, even if it was in her best interest to comply.

Here's what I said to Loretta:

"You don't have to lose weight — you don't even have to live. It's your choice, and I'll respect your decision. No one can force you to do anything, not your parents, not your children, not your friends. They can only hope you do the right thing and encourage you accordingly. You're the master of your own life. Ask yourself the following questions: 'Do I want to die, or do I want to live?' 'Do I want to be fat and feeble, or do I want to be slim and active?' Nobody can tell you what to do with your life. It's entirely up to you."

My message obviously sunk in, for the next day Loretta stuck a note on her refrigerator which read: "What do I choose today?" She resumed her diet, on her own initiative, and was very happy to be losing weight.

Domination

Gwen was 18 years old and still lived with her parents. An accomplished figure skater, she had won several competitions at the age of 15 but was no longer competing actively. The reason: she had put on 45 pounds in recent years and could no longer fit into her skating costume. Both her parents taught figure skating and they wanted their daughter to continue in the sport. It was her mother who sent her to see me.

After the first few weeks on her diet, Gwen began to cheat regularly. She seemed to lack motivation. When I asked her if her desire to compete was strong enough to motivate her, she replied, "Oh yes! I love figure skating." However, when I mentioned that her mother seemed very eager for her to lose weight so she could compete again, she grimaced.

"I want to compete again, I want to look good in my bathing suit next summer, I want the boys to find me attractive, but each time my mother tells me I shouldn't eat this or that, I get stubborn and I eat just to spite her. I know she loves me and that she wants only the best for me, but I can't help myself. I can't stand being told what to do."

Gwen was an adolescent who wanted to stand on her own two feet. To avoid feeling dominated, she refused to do things she was told even if they were in her best interest. Like everyone else, she wanted to feel important; if she thought something was being forced on her, it didn't matter whether it was good or bad, it was a blow to her ego. Gwen thought she was old enough to make her own decisions: if she wanted to do something silly, it was her business.

The weaker, the more fragile our self-image, the more likely we are to feel threatened — we think we have to keep proving to others how strong we are. The stronger our self-image, the more confidence we have — we're not afraid of being dominated and we don't need to show everyone how strong we are.

In order for Gwen to overcome her fear of domination, she had to improve her self-image and build up her confidence. We'll be discussing several self-image improvement techniques in Chapter 21.

It's my life

Annette, 34, was 45 pounds overweight. She'd been trying very hard for six months to lose her excess pounds, when, suddenly, she went on a sugar binge. Here's her story:

During her diet, Annette happened to watch a television program on sugar. It was clearly shown that sugar, of which the average person eats over 120 pounds a year, is a deadly poison. The terrible illnesses caused by excessive sugar consumption were vividly shown on the program; at the top of the list was diabetes, with its host of complications: paralysis, heart attack, and gangrene — often necessitating amputation.

As soon as the program was over, Annette ran to the kitchen, checked to make sure she was alone, and made herself a piece of toast, which she then smothered in strawberry jam. As if that weren't enough, she then poured sugar on top of the jam. Strange behavior, especially from someone whose mother had just died a few months earlier from diabetes caused by obesity, after having both legs amputated for gangrene. Here's how Annette explained her conduct:

"Before the program, I never thought about sugar. My diet was going well and I was very pleased. But while watching the program, even though I kept telling myself, 'Annette, sugar's no good for you — you shouldn't eat any — look what happened to your mother,' another voice inside me said, 'Who are they to tell me what to do? If I want to kill myself with sugar, it's my business.' "

Although the program showed clearly that sugar kills, Annette's reaction was the opposite of what it should have been. Why? Because she wanted to prove to herself that she, and no one else, was in control of her life. "Who do they think they are telling me what I should and shouldn't eat?" she would say to herself. "Just because my mother died of diabetes doesn't mean they can tell me how to run my life. And how do they even know I want to live?''

From speaking with Annette and from her personality test results, I knew she was very passive and that she was afraid to assert herself, especially with her husband. She was married to a good man, but she never expressed her feelings or wishes. Because she never spoke up, her husband decided everything, and she always ended up doing what he wanted.

By eating sugar after she was told it wasn't good for her, Annette was trying to prove that she could stand up for herself. What she had to do was learn to assert herself in a more appropriate way.

Now Annette is finally learning to express her feelings, her desires, her joys, her sorrows. She's learning to say yes and no, to make her own decisions. To express herself is not only her right, it's her duty.

Summary

Reaction is a mental block that consists in rejecting what we feel forced to do and then doing the exact opposite to prove to ourselves that we're fully independent and able to take care of ourselves.

Loretta, 58, felt obliged to lose weight to avoid another heart attack. As soon as her health improved after she lost 50 pounds, she reacted against her cardiologist's ultimatum to lose weight and began to cheat regularly on her diet. Whenever she felt forced to do something, she would recall how she used to be ordered around by her father, who, if she had let him, would have raped her when she was 12.

Now, Loretta realizes that whether she lives or dies is entirely up to her. It is she who decides, each day, what she's going to do with her life.

Gwen, 18, reacted against her mother, even though what her mother wanted for her was in her best interest. Adolescents and young adults need to prove to themselves that they can stand on their own two feet — they need a feeling of importance. For fear of being dominated by another person, they often do the opposite of what's good for them. Many adults never outgrow this rebellious behavior.

To eliminate the need to react against authority, real or imagined, you must develop your confidence and self-esteem. This can be done by setting goals for yourself and then striving to reach them. Gwen repeated to herself every day: "I choose to slim down and to get back into figure skating competition. If my mother feels the same way, so much the better."

Annette never stood up for herself, always living in the shadow of her parents or her husband. For her, this situation was normal. But when a television program told her she couldn't eat sugar, she reacted by going on a sugar binge, just to prove that she couldn't be told what to do. Even though her mother had died from diabetes and had had both her legs amputated, Annette was in no mood to be told how to run her life. If she wanted to kill herself with sugar, it was her business and no one else's.

Now Annette is learning to express herself and to make her own decisions. She's learning to be herself. Soon, she'll no longer feel the need to react whenever she feels obliged to do something.

If you have a reaction block, thc way to eliminate it is to improve your self-image and build up your confidence. You'll no longer need to prove to everyone how strong you are in order to feel important. You are the most important person in your life and you don't need to prove it — to yourself or to anyone else.

CHAPTER 19

FEAR OF FAILURE

Suicide

Dorothy, 38, weighed 264 pounds when she enrolled in my behavior and motivation course about a year ago.

During the first class, I stressed the importance of setting a goal and of keeping in mind the benefits to be derived from attaining it. Since you cannot reach an objective unless you know precisely what that objective is, you must, if you want to slim down, decide upon the weight you wish to attain. But that's not enough. You must also be motivated to reach your objective, which is why you must focus on the advantages of attaining your desired weight. You must concentrate on what you'll gain by slimming down, not on what you'll lose.

I asked the class to imagine themselves at their desired weight, wearing the clothes they'd like to wear, and involved in an activity they enjoy. By visualizing this scene over and over again, as if it were already reality, they would get the necessary motivation to make it so.

But Dorothy refused to visualize herself this way. "I don't want to have dreams that won't come true," she said. "I don't want to suffer needlessly." Although I kept stressing how important it was that she believe in her ability to succeed, she refused to set a goal for herself and to imagine herself as having reached it. She was afraid of failing. She never engaged in any activity unless success was guaranteed. Even when she did get involved in something, she never gave her best; that way, if she failed, she could always use the excuse that she hadn't tried her hardest. She'd been attempting to lose weight for ten years, but had never fully committed herself to any particular program.

Knowing Dorothy's personality, I was surprised to see her taking my course and coming back week after week. Although the course wasn't complicated, it required that she make a commitment to solving her weight problem, something she'd always avoided doing in the past. I explained to her how I saw her problem and asked her why she was attending the course.

"I'll tell you," she replied. "You're right when you say I've never been able to commit myself to a slimming program. And believe me, right now, I'm finding it tough. I almost quit after the first class when you asked me to imagine myself slim. I thought you were superficial. But for some reason, I felt this was my last chance."

"Your last chance for what?"

She hesitated for a moment, then continued: "I wanted to commit suicide, and I thought the best way to do it was to eat myself to death. I couldn't see myself swallowing a bottle of pills or throwing myself in front of a bus — everyone would have known and I would have looked like a fool. But by gorging myself, by destroying my body with food, I could kill myself without anyone knowing it."

"Was your wish to eat yourself to death conscious or unconscious?"

"Oh, it was conscious all right. I knew what I was doing. Coming here was my last chance."

Dorothy's self-esteem had hit rock bottom. One more failure was all it would take to push her over the brink. She would rather die than endure more suffering; indeed, she had already tried to kill herself by overeating.

A year later, however, Dorothy had undergone a complete transformation. By patiently working on her self-image and building up her confidence, she regained her lust for life. She finally committed herself to slimming down and attained her desired weight of 150 pounds. Her dreams of yesterday had become reality.

Never up to it

Rhona, 30, was 100 pounds overweight. After following a balanced, 1,200-calorie diet for three months and taking my behavior course for the same length of time, she lost only four pounds. She wasn't willing to commit herself fully to either the diet or the course: she didn't keep a food diary, and never practiced the relaxation and other techniques I recommended. She seemed to consider a visit to the clinic a social outing. Each week, she had a new excuse or a new mental block to explain why she'd cheated on her diet and hadn't practiced the prescribed techniques.

The first week, Rhona didn't want to lose weight because her 35-year-old boyfriend, with whom she lived, liked women with a lot of meat on their bones. Overweight himself, he brought home chocolates and pastries every day. The second week, she was afraid to lose weight because she didn't think being slim suited her. The third week, she worried about becoming weak from loss of weight. Her job involved heavy labor — she had to push a cart with 16 weighty boxes on it — and she was afraid of losing her strength and being unable to do her work. The fourth week, she was concerned about not being funny any more if she became thin. She liked to make people laugh, and her weight helped her in this respect. The fifth week, it was her fear of failure that was the problem. If she were thin, she might be obliged to try things which her obesity had prevented her from doing. But what if she fell flat on her face? Better to play it safe and remain fat.

Rhona's mother was a former nun who left the order at the age of 40 to get married. She had her only child, Rhona, when she was 42. The father was 59. Being cultured, Rhona's parents introduced her to the arts at a young age. At the age of five, she already weighed 90 pounds and had trouble squeezing into her ballet costume. She was embarrassed to dance in public — she looked so ungraceful lumbering around in a tutu several sizes too small. After a few months, her instructor strongly suggested to her parents that they steer her into another field to which she'd be better suited. If she couldn't cut it as a dancer, perhaps she'd enjoy singing. So they had Rhona take voice lessons, but that didn't work out either.

At the age of 18, Rhona made the first decision of her life: she left home. Another failure. Her parents became ill and blamed her for abandoning them. "How could you be so ungrateful after all we've done for you?" they asked. So she returned home. She'd never been good enough.

Since then, Rhona has always avoided situations where she has to make decisions or assume responsibilities. She's convinced she can't cut it and doesn't want to suffer any more failures like the ones she experienced as a child.

I don't know if Rhona will continue with the program. One thing's for sure: unless she has a desire to change, we won't be able to help her. She has to want to get rid of her fear of failure; she has to want to succeed. Success is easy if you believe in it.

Summary

The fear-of-failure block is more common than one might think. It's known, for example, that before major sports competitions some athletes injure themselves, either on purpose or unconsciously, to avoid having to compete. So traumatized are they by the fear of failure that they'd rather find excuses to withdraw from their event than risk losing. They're afraid of suffering a failure which would weaken their already poor self-images. They're like the ostrich that hides its head in the sand to avoid seeing. But trying to escape from reality is never the answer.

Just because you fail at something doesn't mean you're a failure as a person. To err is human, and it's by making errors that you develop and grow. The more mistakes you make, the more opportunities you have to improve yourself. Just think how much better you'd be if you improved yourself just one percent for each mistake you made.

Dorothy's self-esteem was so low that one more failure would have completely destroyed her. Rather than continue suffering, she decided to put an end to her life by eating herself to death. Our behavior and motivation course was her last hope. Fortunately, by working on her self-image, we were able to rekindle her love for life so that she was no longer afraid of failure.

Rhona avoided making decisions and taking on responsibilities because she felt she couldn't succeed at anything. She had been traumatized by her past failures — starting with her bitter experience in ballet school at the age of five — and didn't want to suffer any more disappointments. However, there was hope for her. By programming herself properly, she could, in time, overcome her fear of failure — if she wanted to.

Success is easy if you believe in it.

CHAPTER 20

FEAR OF SUCCESS

Reborn at 50

Shirley, 50, was 60 pounds overweight. After dieting for a few weeks without cheating, she began to complain that she missed sugar a lot. A few weeks later, she was ready to explode: all she ever thought about were cakes, pies, and pastries — she even dreamed about sweets.

Seeing the frustration building up inside her, I told Shirley I had no objection to her eating some sweets.

"But doctor," she replied, "I don't have the right to cheat. On all my previous diets, I always quit the first time I cheated. I'd like to stay on my diet longer this time."

"Look, nobody's perfect. It's normal for a person on a diet to cheat once in a while. Rarely have I had a patient go through an entire diet without once indulging herself. I remember a patient of mine who stuck to her diet religiously for five months — I had to send her to a psychiatrist because she had an obsessive personality that was destroying her. With her it was always one extreme or another — there was never any happy medium. You have the right to cheat now and then, but not to give up. Cheating on your diet is a small mistake that will enable you to understand yourself better. You shouldn't overdo it, of course, but if you do happen to cheat on your diet, you should try to learn from the experience to improve yourself."

Shirley seemed reassured by the idea that it was all right to cheat once in a while, that it was perfectly normal to do so, and that she didn't have to give up her diet just because of a momentary lapse.

"I'd like you to try this test," I continued. "Right now, you're very frustrated because you haven't eaten anything sweet for almost two months. If you do decide to indulge your sweet tooth, try to make a distinction between the taste of what you eat and how you feel about it. First listen to what your taste buds say, then to what your mind says. We'll discuss the matter again during your next visit."

The following week, Shirley entered my office with a broad smile on her face. "Your test worked," she said. "I was invited to my sister's on the weekend, and she prepared a delicious cheesecake for the occasion. I used to love cheesecake before I started my diet. Then I remembered what you told me about it being normal to cheat once in a while. Since I didn't want to go crazy and end up on some psychiatrist's couch like that patient you mentioned, I decided to have some cake. The first mouthful was divine — the best cheesecake I'd ever eaten. How could I have gone without it for so long? I savored every morsel. Then, when I returned home, I thought about the test you asked me to do, you know, about making a distinction between how the food tasted and what I thought about it. Well, you were right — the cheesecake was too rich. I even had trouble digesting it. It tasted much better in the past."

Shirley had just discovered that she tasted more with her mind than with her mouth. It's like that with everyone. If you go without your favorite food for about three weeks, your taste for that food should change. If it still tastes sensational after three weeks of doing without, it's because you *think* it still tastes great. The mind is stronger than the taste buds.

For two months, Shirley felt deprived of her only joy in life: eating sweets. Like everyone else, she wanted some gratification now and then. Her husband had been suffering from heart disease for 15 years and hadn't worked for a long time. The slightest aggravation or exertion gave him angina pains. Because he was very anxious and afraid of dying, he didn't want Shirley to leave the house, especially after she herself was ordered to rest by her doctor because of a shoulder injury she suffered at work. After physiotherapy failed to improve her condition, her doctor suggested an operation, but she refused. Shirley felt her life wasn't worth it — her only joy was eating sweets.

I tried to show Shirley that despite her difficult situation, she could get more out of her life than just eating pastries — if she wanted to. She seemed receptive to the idea, but something was blocking her. We found out what it was on her next visit.

"I think I know what's been blocking me, but I feel uncomfortable talking about it," she said. "I've felt stifled for so long that I'm afraid of what I might do if I get down to my ideal weight. I think I'll explode — I've so much catching up to do. The trouble is, I'm worried about my husband — if he suffers another heart attack because of me, I'll never forgive myself. I couldn't do that to him — he's always been so good to me."

Shirley was afraid of success and how it would affect her. So frustrated was she in her current situation that she was afraid of how she'd react if she lost weight. What if her husband suffered?

I told Shirley she had no right to destroy herself because of someone else. The only person she could live for was herself. She couldn't live for her mother, her father, her husband, or anyone else. Moreover, by learning to live more for herself, she wouldn't be hurting her husband, she'd be doing him a favor. A depressed person can't help but depress those around him; a happy person, on the other hand, makes others happy.

I finally persuaded Shirley that she had the right to be happy. For one month, I had her practice an autosuggestion technique for weight reduction which I'd recorded on cassette. The technique stressed the fact that everyone is entitled to success. The results were extraordinary. "I feel reborn," she said happily. "I was dead before."

Now that she had finally realized how wonderful life could be, Shirley decided to have her injured shoulder operated on. Her life was worth it now — food was no longer her only joy. At the age of 50, she had discovered life.

Fear of looking good

Juanita was single and lived alone in an apartment. Twenty-seven years old, she weighed 201 pounds, almost twice her ideal weight. I met her at a party given by some friends of mine. Her attire left a lot to be desired, and her hair, although clean, looked as if it hadn't been combed in mouths. As often occurs at parties, the conversation turned to the latest diet fad. Juanita took a radical stand: she was against any kind of diet — although she certainly could have used one.

"I want to be loved for myself, not for my body," she said. "I have many good friends who love me for who I am, and I'm afraid I might lose their friendship if I were slimmer. They'd be more interested in my body than in me."

Juanita explained that her best friend was a man who lived with another woman. She truly enjoyed his company, but was afraid he'd become interested in her sexually if she lost weight.

Juanita had built a life based on intellectual development and friendship, while completely ignoring her physical and sexual side. When I expressed the idea that one's body was an integral part of one's being, and that purposely and consciously rejecting one's physical, intellectual, or spiritual side was tantamount to self-mutilation, to a lack of respect for oneself as a human being, she asked me if I would still love my wife "if she were covered with pimples."

"If my wife were afflicted with a skin disease, I'd certainly be distressed, but I'd still love her. I'd help her cope with her condition as best I could. The important thing is, she'd still have her self-respect, for it wouldn't be her fault that she had the disease. But if she didn't respect herself, I don't think I could respect her. If someone doesn't care enough about himself to develop his full potential, how can he expect another person to love him? I love my wife. She's given me a lot of happiness. She's always encouraged me in all my endeavours and she's given me three wonderful children. She respects herself and makes the most of her abilities. Were she to become fat because of illness, I'd love her just as much and help her deal with her condition. However, were she to lose her self-respect, were she to become fat through neglect and make no effort to improve herself, I don't think I could love her as much."

After a while, Juanita and I found ourselves alone in a corner, continuing our conversation. "If I were thin," she said, "I don't know what I would do." She hesitated for a moment, then continued, "I think I'd have men running after me."

The truth was finally coming out. Juanita was deeply frustrated by her obesity and her repressed sexuality. Now she was afraid of what she might do if she lost weight.

Juanita was also afraid of having to undergo cosmetic surgery on her breasts, which were drooping. Just the idea of being operated on scared her to death.

Juanita was afraid of success. She was afraid that if she lost weight, her friendships would crumble; she was afraid of becoming a mindless sex-object; she was afraid of undergoing surgery. All these fears were preventing her from seeking success. Instead, she settled for occasional happiness. When we parted, she looked pensive and said she might come to see me for her problem.

Because of her fears — mostly irrational — Juanita put unnecessary limitations on herself. Her potential was boundless, yet she remained paralyzed by her lack of self-confidence. She needed to eliminate her fears which were preventing her from being herself. She had to believe in herself and program herself positively to develop her full potential.

People are happy only when they exploit their abilities to the fullest.

Nothing for me

Isabel, 22, was a cheerful, pretty young woman. For her obesity problem — she was 30 pounds overweight — Isabel always looked for a miracle cure. If after three weeks of dieting she hadn't lost at least 15 pounds, she gave up. When I asked her why she'd decided to go on a diet again, she told me she wanted to be a stewardess and that her chances of being hired would be much better if she were at her ideal weight.

After one month on a protein diet, Isabel lost 20 pounds. Everything was going well: she looked great, she didn't feel hungry, she was full of pep, and she was very happy. Then, suddenly, she dropped her diet without explanation.

I saw Isabel again a few months later at a business meeting. She had slimmed down and had become a lawyer. She didn't recognize me at all.

"You probably met my sister," she said. "We're identical twins. The only difference between us is our weight. She's obese."

"Do you have any idea why Isabel quit her diet when it was going so well?" I asked.

"Oh, she always gives up near the end. She's tried countless diets in the past, but she never sticks them out. It's the same with everything. She changes jobs two or three times a year. With her personality, she has no trouble finding a job, but as soon as she gets a promotion — she never asks for one — she quits without a word of explanation. Just recently she dropped out of her flight attendant's course. As for her diet, as soon as she lost some weight, men began asking her out, so she panicked and quit."

Each time Isabel was about to succeed at her job, with her weight problem, or in her relationships with men, she gave up. She was afraid of success and considered herself unworthy of it. Although she was very fond of her twin sister, she'd always felt inferior to her, despite the fact they both had the same education and that their mother had done her best not to show any preference. Isabel had always taken her sister as a model and wanted to be just like her, even though she knew it was impossible. She felt her sister had inherited all the good qualities and she none, for her sister was successful in all her endeavors, both personal and professional, while she, Isabel, failed at everything. Because she considered herself worthless, it was almost impossible for her to succeed. Whenever she did happen to do well at something, she never took the credit. "I was just lucky," she'd say. And if someone complimented her, she felt they either wanted to take advantage of her or didn't want to hurt her feelings. She thought and acted like a loser.

Isabel had to stop comparing herself to her twin sister and stop wanting to be like her. She, too, had inherited many fine qualities — not necessarily the same ones as her sister's, but fine qualities just the same; her potential was just as great. Although they were twins, each had her own personality and her own talents. There was enough room at the top for both of them, although the paths they took to get there might be entirely different.

In order to build up her self-confidence, Isabel had to move away from her sister, with whom she was living, and start taking on her own responsibilities. She also needed to improve her self-image by employing the techniques discussed in the following chapter. She had the potential to succeed, and as much right to as anyone else.

Success is a habit, that of not giving up until you've reached your goal.

Millionaire

Frank, 36, was 80 pounds overweight. His obesity bothered him a great deal. Because he lacked energy and was always short of breath, he had to refuse whenever his children asked him to play ball — he simply couldn't keep up with them.

Fed up, Frank decided to go on a crash diet to lose his excess weight. He shed 60 pounds in the first three months, but was unable to make any further progress. One week he'd lose weight, the next week he'd gain it back. I asked him what was blocking him.

"I know I can get down to my ideal weight," he said. "I've only a few pounds to go. But it seems I'm afraid of not being able to maintain my ideal weight once I reach it. I don't feel confident enough yet, so I'm marking time."

Although Frank no longer felt hungry and had overcome several bad habits, including a craving for rich foods, he couldn't get below 200 pounds. For two months, he continued his little game: up five pounds one week, down five the next. Then he started to get depressed. Week after week, his depression worsened, but he wouldn't tell me what was bothering him. One day, it finally came out: his business was going bankrupt. Out of the blue, his creditors demanded that he pay up immediately everything he owed, this despite the fact that his business was going quite well. It was not until two weeks later that he admitted it was his own father who had driven him to bankruptcy, for it was he who was his largest creditor. Not only did his father ask for his own money back, but he put pressure on the bank not to lend Frank any more funds. He didn't like the way his son was running his business and vowed to put him under. Everything Frank owned was repossessed, even his car.

At the age of 36, Frank lost everything he owned, everything he'd worked for. One hundred thousand dollars, twenty years of work, down the drain. And he had a wife and two children to support. But what was even harder for him to accept was his failure as a man. The way he saw it, for a father to do in his son the way his father had, the son must deserve it. Obviously, he wasn't worthy of his father's love.

Frank's problem could be traced to his childhood. He'd never felt loved at home. Even when he was eight years old, it didn't bother his parents if he didn't come home for three days. They separated when he was twelve and sent him to live with his aunt, with whom he remained for four years. Despite everything, Frank had great admiration for his father and wanted to be just like him. To him, his father was a symbol of strength, courage, and self-confidence. For seven years Frank never heard from his father, but this absence only increased his father's stature in his eyes. The more he missed his father, the more he idealized him. To be punished now by his father not only pained Frankly deeply, it confirmed to him his own failure as a man.

Frank had always felt worthless, and because he felt that way, he acted that way. In everything he did, he always settled for the minimum. He considered it his duty to provide his wife and children with the bare necessities, but once this obligation was fulfilled, Frank was satisfied. He didn't think he deserved anything more, least of all personal success. He had already owned two other businesses, but each time success was within his grasp, he found all kinds of excuses to give up. He was afraid of success and didn't think he deserved it, because his father had always told him he wouldn't amount to anything. Each failure he suffered was further proof that his father was right.

After two months under my care, Frank finally saw the light. "The bankruptcy was the best thing that could have happened to me," he said.

His friends thought he was crazy. How could someone who'd just gone through a bankruptcy be so happy about what had happened to him? But Frank had reason to be happy, for he was now a "millionaire." He'd just discovered the incredible riches within him, the great potential that had remained dormant for years. He finally realized that it's not what our parents think of us that determines our worth. Our parents can program us well or they can program us poorly, they can help us develop our abilities or not help us at all, but our potential to succeed is always there, with or without their approval. Of course, our parents play an important role in our programming because we look up to them when we're young and believe everything they tell us, even if their ideas are harebrained. However, when we reach adulthood, we can think for ourselves and decide if what we were taught is good or bad for us. If it's bad, we can then reprogram ourselves positively.

Frank no longer puts limits on himself; he always wants to go further and further. His behavior at home has changed too: he's much more patient and understanding with his wife and children. He understands himself better and loves himself more, and is able to extend that love and understanding to others. Before, he used to become aggressive whenever he or anyone else made a mistake; today, he accepts mistakes as part of life and laughs about them. He doesn't hate his father now; instead, he pities him. When his friends ask him about his new outlook on life, he says: "Before, I was in the race, but I was stuck in neutral and never reached the finish line; now, I've changed gears and I'm going to win the race!"

Summary

When I ask someone, "Are you afraid of success?" the answer I usually get is: "Are you kidding? Of course not!" When you ask yourself this question, wait a moment before answering and take a good look at your behavior. All of us carry around an image of ourselves which is shaped by our education, our past experiences, and the society in which we live. If our self-image is that of a loser, we're doomed to failure: we consider ourselves incapable of succeeding and of handling the responsibilities that come with success.

Shirley was afraid of what she would do if she slimmed down. She was particularly worried about how her husband would react if she started to assert herself: what if he suffered another heart attack because of her? Fortunately, by practicing autosuggestion, Shirley developed her self-confidence and learned to live for herself. She discovered happiness and can now share her newfound joy with others.

Juanita was afraid of being loved for her body rather than for herself, so she neglected her body as much as possible. She was riddled with unreasonable fears which prevented her from being herself. She was afraid of her sexuality, and she was afraid of undergoing cosmetic breast surgery. Instead of living life to the hilt, she settled for a few momentary pleasures. I'm confident she will in time be able to rid herself of her irrational fears and to realize her full potential.

Isabel had always underestimated herself because she thought her twin sister had inherited all the good qualities and she none. She had to stop comparing herself to her sister and wanting to be like her. Once she realized she had strong points of her own, her self-confidence would grow.

Frank had to suffer through two bankruptcies before he started to believe in himself and in success. At the age of 36, he lost everything he owned, including his self-respect. Even his father didn't love him. After a while, though, Frank realized that going bankrupt was the best thing that could have happened to him. He became aware of his own self-worth and changed gears in mid-life. He feels like a million dollars.

CHAPTER 21

ON THE ROAD TO SUCCESS

Role of the self-image

The greatest discovery of this century in the field of psychology was that of the self-image. We all carry within us a picture of how we see ourselves, with our strengths and weaknesses. We can fool others into believing we're something we're not, but we can't fool ourselves. For each activity we do, we evaluate our abilities; for example, we may believe we're good in math, average in tennis, excellent in public speaking, lousy at cards, and terrible at maintaining a diet. It all depends on how well or poorly we do when we try these activities. This evaluation of our strengths and weaknesses, of our good points and bad, constitutes our self-image.

Our self-image is a reflection of how we think of ourselves. If we've never played golf before, we assume that we can't shoot a 68 the first time out. If we've experienced failures in the past in a certain endeavor, such as following a diet, we think we aren't up to the task and have no confidence in our ability to succeed. Our self-image is thus based on our past experiences, on how we view our successes and failures, our triumphs and humiliations. Our childhood experiences are of particular importance in the formation of our self-image.

Two important discoveries pertaining to the self image have radically changed our way of understanding and improving human behavior.

1) All our actions are *always* determined by our self-image. We are what we think we are. If you think you're not good at golf, either because you've never played before or because you have played but very poorly, you won't have confidence in your ability to succeed at golf and you'll play like a duffer. To take another example, if you think you can't lose weight because all your past diets ended in failure, whenever you begin a new diet you'll be convinced from the start that you won't succeed and, inevitably, you'll fail, thus reinforcing your belief that you can't lose weight. It's a vicious circle. If you're convinced you're going to fail, you will, no matter how good your intentions. People who fail on diet after diet don't fail for want of trying, but because their poor self-image dooms them to failure.

2) Our self-image can be changed. Victor Seribriakoff was, until the age of 32, a nobody. He continually changed jobs, unable to hold even the simplest one. When he was 15, his teacher told him he wasn't too bright and that he'd have a hard time making it; he even suggested that Victor drop out of school because he was such a hopeless case. Convinced he was good for nothing, Victor spent the next 17 years fulfilling his teacher's prophecy of failure. At the age of 32, it just so happened that Victor had to write an intelligence test for a job he'd applied for. His score: 161. Victor was a genius. You can guess what

happened. Convinced he was a genius, Victor begain to act like one. He started writing books, came up with several inventions, and became a wealthy businessman. His most spectacular achievement: he was elected president of MENSA, an international society of geniuses whose sole criterion for admission is an I.Q. of at least 140.

Until the age of 32, Victor thought he was a failure and acted like one. When he scored high on his I.Q. test, his self-image was transformed and he began to act like the genius he knew he was.

The majority of the obese patients you've read about in the preceding chapters who finally managed to lose weight were able to do so because they changed their self-image. In my fifteen years of medical practice, I've seen several patients fail, but very few who couldn't succeed. Once people overcome their mental blocks and reprogram their subconscious in a positive way, they find that success comes easily.

Role of the imagination

Right now you may be saying to yourself: "Sure, I'd like to change my self-image, but you're telling me that I've been programmed negatively by my past failures and that it's impossible for me to have positive experiences as long as I have this negative image of myself. You say I need to experience successes to program myself positively, but that I can't have any because I've been programmed negatively. How can I break out of this vicious circle?" There is a way.

A few years ago, scientists conducted the following experiment: they assembled a group of people in a room and connected them to an electroencephalograph, a device that detects and records brain waves. Then they exposed the subjects to various stimuli: a screaming woman, a gunshot, and a dog running across the room. Not unexpectedly, these stimuli elicited stressful reactions from the subjects, as was evidenced by their brain waves. The experiment was then repeated, but this time the subjects were blindfolded and asked to simply imagine a screaming woman, a gunshot, and a dog running across the room. Interestingly, the same brain wave patterns were registered by the electroencephalograph as when the subjects had been exposed to the real stimuli. Scientists were able to conclude from this experiment that the brain functions much like a computer in that it makes no distinction between a real experience and one that is imagined.

This discovery had important repercussions, for it was now thought that an individual might be able to program himself positively and improve his self-image by simply *imagining* personal success.

To prove this theory, scientists at the University of Chicago tried an experiment. Students were divided into three groups and their basketball-shooting skills were tested. The first group was then asked to practice shooting baskets every day for one hour, the second group not to practice at all, and the third to spend one hour a day just imagining themselves sinking baskets. After 30 days, the subjects' shooting skills were tested once again. Those who had practiced one hour a day improved their performance by 24 percent, while those who hadn't practiced at all showed no improvement. Amazingly, those who had practiced only in their head improved their performance by 23 percent, almost the same degree of improvement as those who had actually practiced shooting hoops. Practice in the imagination had thus proved just as beneficial as real practice.

Setting your goal

What is success? By definition, it's the attainment of a goal you've set for yourself. It's impossible to be successful if you don't have an objective. Try to find something you're not looking for or reach some destination you're not trying to get to. Ridiculous, you say, and yet I see hundreds of patients who begin a diet without setting a specific goal for themselves. "I don't know how much I'd like to weigh," they'll say. "I'll see as I go along." Or: "I just want to feel better." "I'd like to look better in my clothes." "I want to please my husband."

You can find only what you're looking for. If you have a vague goal, your success will be vague as well. Try the following experiment: the next time you search for something in your house, take a good look at your behavior. You'll notice that you concentrate on what you're looking for and don't even notice the other things you see. Try the same experiment the next time you look for a name in the telephone book — see if you can recall any of the names you come across which you weren't trying to find. Couldn't remember any, could you?

The only way to improve your self-image and to succeed in life (and to lose weight) is to set a goal for yourself. Here are some important guidelines which may help:

1) The goal you set for yourself must be important to you. If it's not important, you won't have the necessary motivation to attain it. Ask yourself: "What will I gain by losing weight? What will I be able to do that I can't do now? What will I be able to do better and for a longer time? Focus on the benefits you'll derive from attaining your goal — they're the key to your motivation.

2) To solve your weight problem, you must decide how much you'd like to weigh. Don't set your target weight too high for fear of not being able to lose the necessary pounds. If, by magic, you could weigh exactly what you wanted, how much would you weigh? (While you shouldn't be afraid of setting a tough goal for yourself,

don't be unrealistic either: the goal you establish must be attainable.)

3) Give yourself enough time to reach your goal.

4) If you set a lofty goal for yourself that will take many months to reach, break it down into a series of smaller goals, each of which can be attained in one month's time.

For example, if you decided to build a house, you'd proceed step by step: first you'd lay the foundation, then you'd build the framework, then you'd install the plumbing, and so on and so forth. Building a new personality is like building a new house — you must break the job down into a series of smaller tasks. Before you start, if you look at the end result you're aiming for, it may seem impossible. However, if you divide the work you have to do into tasks of a more manageable size, you'll probably find your goal is quite feasible after all. When I started working on this book, I had 300 pages to write by hand. I thought it would take forever. But when I broke the job down into smaller units, I saw it wouldn't be that difficult at all. If I wrote 20 pages a week, I'd be finished in 15 weeks. The 20 pages a week could be broken down further into four pages a day, five days a week. Since I averaged two pages an hour, I had to write only two hours a day to complete my book in 15 weeks. I actually finished it in less time than that.

You should tackle your weight problem the same way I approached this book. First, figure out how many pounds you have to lose to attain your ideal weight, without worrying about how difficult it may be. Then, set yourself a goal of losing five or six pounds a month, *but never more*. This means you'll have to lose only 1 ⅔ pounds a week, which can be accomplished by reducing your diet by only 500 calories a day. If that still seems too difficult, try cutting only 250 calories a day from your diet and allow yourself twice as much time to reach your desired weight.

If you think cutting 500 calories a day is too easy, good for you, but don't try to make things too difficult for yourself. At the beginning, you may lose weight twice as fast as you'd anticipated, but it's better to be ahead of schedule because you may reach a point where the pounds don't come off that easily. It's wiser to set reasonable goals for yourself and to chalk up a series of successes than to set difficult goals which may result in failures and frustration. There's always the danger that in reading this book, you'll become overly enthusiastic and want to go too quickly. But it serves no purpose to set an unrealistic goal for yourself, for your chances of succeeding will be slim. It's all right to dream big, as long as your dream is feasible. You must have both the time and the means to attain your goal. Often, it's a good idea to get the opinion of another person who will be able to look at your situation in a more objective way. In general, if you think you'll be able to reach your goal within a certain period of time, you should allow yourself twice that. You're better off climbing one easy step at a time than trying to take two or three at a bound. It's by ringing up many small victories that your confidence and self-esteem will grow.

5) Be specific when establishing your goal. You must know as clearly as possible what you want to accomplish. "I want to feel better" doesn't mean anything. However, if you see: "I want to ride my bicycle at my ideal weight, look good in my bathing suit next summer, go jogging, and feel young at ?," then you have a specific goal that you can attain. You know what you're looking for.

6) Your goal must be personal. Nobody — neither your parents, nor your children, nor your spouse — can impose a goal on you. *You* must choose your own goals to

have any chance of succeeding. You're the only person responsible for your behavior and your life. If the decision to lose weight isn't your own, stop immediately — you're wasting your time. You won't have the necessary motivation to overcome the difficulties along the way and you'll suffer another failure, which will only reinforce your loser image. Ask yourself: "Do I want to slim down for myself or for someone else?"

7) You're not perfect, so don't expect to attain your goal without making mistakes along the way. Instead, try to learn from your mistakes to improve yourself. If for each error, you bettered yourself by just 10 percent, you'd be assured of success after only 10 errors.

The next time you drive your car, pay close attention to your actions. Even if you're driving along a straight road, you'll notice that you must continually correct the direction of the car, first one way, then the other, to keep it on the road. It's the sum of all these small corrections that gets you where you want to go.

Guided missiles operate on the same principle. When radar indicates that a missile is off course, its trajectory is adjusted to get it back on track. It's by making a series of small corrections, or zigzags, that the missile is able to reach its target.

Walt Disney went bankrupt seven times before he finally succeeded. He kept his goal in mind and learned from each failure so that he could eventually make his dream come true. Were it not for his failures, there would be no Disney World today.

When you start out, keep in mind that you'll inevitably make mistakes, but that you'll be able to learn from them to correct your course and attain your goal. You're allowed to make errors and cheat on your diet, but you're not allowed to give up. You're the only one who is responsible for your errors and you must live with the consequences, but feeling guilty when you foul up is another story. Guilt is a negative emotion which serves no purpose. Instead of being torn by guilt when you make a mistake, try to take advantage of it to better yourself. Discover the pride and satisfaction that comes with self-improvement.

8) Attaining your goals doesn't depend on luck. You're responsible for your successes and your failures. Practice makes perfect: it's by lifting weights that you become strong, and it's by setting goals for yourself and not giving up that you'll succeed. There's no such thing as luck.

While rereading this chapter, take a pencil and paper and jot down the goals you wish to attain. It's very important that you do so, for writing down your goals will make them clearer to you. Repeat this exercise at least once a month.

Another thing you should do is divide your goals into three categories: outside goals, family goals (if applicable), and personal goals. Your outside goals can include things you'd like to accomplish at work or during your leisure hours; your family goals will be the kind of relationships you'd like to establish with your spouse, your children, or your parents; your personal goals will include such things as how much weight you'd like to lose, the shape you'd like to be in, the bad habits you'd like to overcome. Keep these goals to yourself — don't go blabbing about them to everyone. There are too many negative people who will try to discourage you.

Dreaming of success

Once your goals have been established, it's time to put your imagination to work. Your imagination is an extraordinary tool that will help you succeed. In the past, psychotherapy was based on dredging up memories from the past; with our new methods of treatment, however, the emphasis is on the future and the imagination. The results are fantastic.

When Neil Armstrong first set foot on the moon, he said he felt as if he'd already been there, having imagined the scene vividly for four years before his flight. Great musicians and conductors often go over in their minds beforehand the scores they're going to interpret. Famous athletes like skier Jean-Claude Killy and golfer Jack Nicklaus often "practice in their heads" to perfect their skills. By going over a particular technique in their heads over and over again, they're able to execute it automatically in competition. The more a great musician plays automatically, without thinking, the better he is. The same goes for a fine athlete.

Colonel George Hall spent seven years in a 3 × 6 foot prison cell in Vietnam. To maintain his sanity, he played golf — a sport at which he excelled — every day in his head. He played in his imagination as if he were actually out on the course: he scrutinized the position of his ball, checked the wind direction, and selected his clubs with the utmost care. Back in the United States after his liberation, in his first round of golf in seven years, George Hall shot a 76, a score worthy of a professional who practices every day. By working on his game in his mind, he had honed his skills and developed his self-confidence to the point where he didn't even have to think about his technique — it had become automatic.

To attain the goals you've set for yourself, try to see yourself in your mind as you'd like to be. For your weight problem, picture yourself at your desired weight, wearing the clothes you'd like to wear, while engaging in some activity you enjoy. Imagine the scene as vividly as possible — take in all the surroundings: the sights, the sounds, the smells. Try to capture the feeling of well-being and satisfaction you'll get upon reaching your goal. Go over this scene in your mind as often as possible, at least every morning upon awakening and every evening upon retiring. One of my patients pictured herself slim, dancing the night away; another saw herself riding horseback in the country. The possibilities are endless. What's important is to picture a situation that *you* would like to be in and to make it as vivid and as real as possible. Then repeat the scene in your mind as often as you can until you've reached your goal.

Some people may raise the objection that they've already had goals which they dreamed of but that they never attained them and became even more unhappy. They say they're no longer interested in pipe dreams. Again, I must stress the importance of having realistic goals. I also firmly believe in the value of dreams. On average, we dream four times a night, with each period lasting anywhere from 10 to 60 minutes. Between 20 and 30 percent of our sleep time is spent dreaming. Numerous studies have shown just how important dreaming is to our well-being.

In one particular study, sleeping subjects were awakened as soon as they began dreaming, then permitted to go back to sleep. The purpose of this was to deprive them of dreaming, while allowing them enough sleep. After 72 hours of dream deprivation, almost all the subjects showed symptoms of psychological disorders, ranging from paranoia to schizophrenia. We obviously need to dream at night.

But what about dreaming during the daytime? Is that important too? I think it is, for at the beginning it's the only way we can experience the successes we need to improve our self-image so we can eventually succeed in real life. Walt Disney failed many times, but in the end he succeeded because he had a dream. All great inventions were first a dream in someone's mind before they became reality.

Without dreams, without creative imagination, mankind cannot progress. Neither can you.

One day at a time

Several times a day, you should picture in your mind the goal you wish to attain, as if it were already reality. Then you should go about attaining your objective, *one day at a time.*

The main reason people fail is that they try to go too fast. They want to finish before they even start. But Rome wasn't built in a day. It took several months, perhaps even several years, for you to gain your extra pounds, so give yourself enough time to lose them. Don't set yourself such a tight deadline that you've no room for error; you don't even have to have a deadline at all. Try to reach your goal one step at a time — it's amazing what you can accomplish if you persevere. So often, I've seen people fail because they wanted to go too fast. They try to take two or three steps at a bound and end up falling flat on their face. Don't forget, it's by chalking up a lot of small victories that you'll build up your confidence and develop a winning attitude.

Your worst enemy

Physically and mentally, we have everything we need to succeed. Unfortunately, many people use only a fraction of their potential. They put limitations on themselves because of ignorance, laziness, or fear. Are you one of these people? If so, you musn't ignore the power within you any longer. It's easy to become lazy in our consumer society, but laziness is not the way to happiness. You can't be happy doing nothing. If you're unhappy now, do something — you've got nothing to lose and everything to gain. Don't confuse fear with prudence. Prudence can help you make a wise decision; fear, on the other hand, is a negative emotion that prevents you from fulfilling your potential. Get rid of your fears and start believing in yourself. You were born to succeed. Don't settle for less when you can have more. Don't be one of those people who spend their whole lives complaining and feeling sorry for themselves. Don't put limitations on yourself. Go for it!

Alpha power

There are four different kinds of brain waves as registered by the electroencephalograph: alpha, beta, delta, and theta. Delta waves, which have a frequency of 1 to 3 cycles per second, occur during deep sleep, when the brain is functioning very slowly. Theta waves are prevalent during the dream state and have a frequency of 4 to 7 cycles per second. In the half-awake state, it is alpha waves, with a frequency of 8 to 12 cycles per second, that predominate. Beta waves, whose frequency ranges from 13 to 26 cycles per second, occur during the waking state, when the brain is functioning very rapidly. (See Figure 6)

Figure 6

BRAIN-WAVE FREQUENCIES

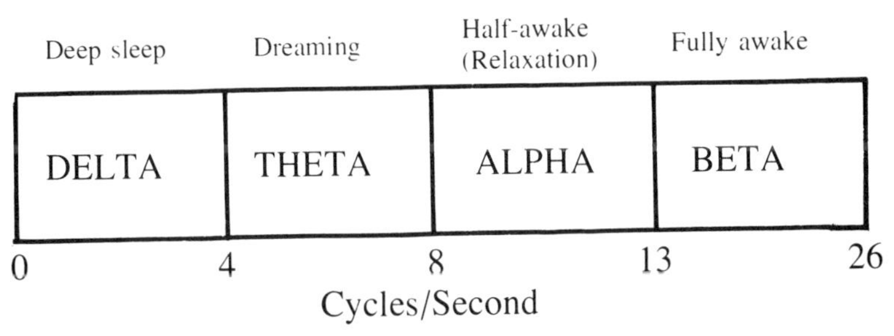

Several studies have been conducted on brain waves and their related states. We now know that alpha waves are associated with a state of serenity and well-being. They occur when we're deeply relaxed, with eyes closed, but disappear as soon as we open our eyes. Alpha waves also occur when we're about to fall asleep, vanishing when we go into a deep sleep.

Some people are better able to attain the alpha state than others. Those who can produce alpha waves easily have been shown to be faster learners than those who can't; they also have better memories. Because of its various characteristics, the alpha state is highly conducive to the visualization and self-programming techniques discussed earlier. What's more, almost all of us (92 percent) can learn to induce the alpha state as often as we want. All it takes is 20 minutes of practice a day for 20 days. Once trained, we can induce the desired state in five to ten minutes.

Among the methods used to induce the alpha state are transcendental meditation, yoga, and various relaxation techniques such as progressive relaxation and autogenic training. I usually have my patients use one of the relaxation techniques. I lend them a cassette with which they can learn to relax and have them practice for 20 minutes a day. After three weeks, most of my patients master the technique and are able to induce the alpha state.

For those of you who may not be able to obtain a relaxation method on cassette, you'll find in the following pages a brief description of the autogenic training technique. You should be able to obtain satisfactory results after a month of practice, but don't worry if it takes you longer. You may not be able to feel heaviness in your arms and legs before three or four weeks, and it may take you six to eight weeks to feel warmth in your limbs. Your rate of progress will depend on how nervous or stressed you are to begin with, as well as on how often you practice the technique. If you're not progressing as quickly as you'd like, you may wish to increase your number of training sessions to two or three a day.

Autogenic training

First week

1- Assume a comfortable position (seated or reclining).

2- Make sure the surroundings are quiet (take the phone off the hook).

3- Your clothing should be loose and unrestrictive.

4- Close your eyes.

5- Breathing exercise:
   - As you inhale deeply, fill your abdomen with air, then your thorax.
   - Tuck in your tummy.
   - Keep the air in your lungs for four or five seconds.
   - With tummy tucked in, exhale slowly.
   - Repeat three times.

6- Repeat to yourself ten times:
   - My right arm is heavy.
   - My right arm is very heavy.
   - My left arm is heavy.
   - My left arm is very heavy.
   - Both my arms are heavy and warm.

7- Repeat to yourself three times:
   - Everything is normal.

8- Stand up and walk around for about thirty seconds.

9- Repeat each exercise three times per session.

10- Do three sessions per day, if possible.

Second week

1- Same position and setting.

2- Breathing exercise (3 times).

3- Repeat to yourself five times:
   - Both my arms are heavy and warm.

4- Repeat to yourself ten times:
   - My right leg is heavy.
   - My right leg is very heavy.
   - My left leg is heavy.
   - My left leg is very heavy.
   - Both my legs are heavy and warm.

5- Repeat to yourself three times:
   - Everything is normal.

6- Repeat each exercise three times per session, with a 30-second break between exercises.

7- Do three sessions per day, if possible.

Third week

1- Same position and setting.

2- Breathing exercise (3 times).

3- Repeat to yourself five times:
   - Both my arms are heavy and warm.
   - Both my legs are heavy and warm.

4- Repeat to yourself ten times:
   - My eyelids are heavy.
   - My eyelids are very heavy.
   - My jaw is heavy.
   - My jaw is very heavy.
   - My forehead is cool.

5- Repeat to yourself three times:
   - Everything is normal.

6- Repeat each exercise three times per session.

7- Do three sessions per day, if possible.

Fourth week and the following weeks

1- Same position and setting.

2- Breathing exercise (3 times).

3- Count to yourself;

1 to 5:	Both my arms are heavy and warm.
6 to 10:	Both my legs are heavy and warm.
11 and 12:	My eyelids are heavy.
13 and 14:	My jaw is heavy.
15:	My forehead is cool.
16 to 20:	With each breath I take, my arms (legs, eyelids . . .) are getting heavier and heavier.

4- Repeat to yourself four times:
- Everything is normal.

At the end of your third or fourth week of training, or when you begin to feel warmth in your limbs, you may start using your imagination and the power of suggestion to reprogram yourself for success.

Work on only one goal at a time. For example, you may wish to spend the first month focussing on a personal goal you wish to attain. Make up one or two short sentences similar to those listed below and repeat them to yourself several times a day for one or two minutes while in the alpha state. At the same time, try to picture yourself as having already attained your goal. Here are some examples of suggestive sentences you may wish to use:

To lose weight:
I'm getting thin and I feel good.
I like to be thin.
I feel younger.
I like to be thin — I like to feel good.

To take one day at a time:
I feel better when I take one day at a time.

It's easy, one day at a time.
I like to feel better and I take one day at a time.

To learn from your mistakes:
I learn from my mistakes.
I have the right to cheat.
I improve from my mistakes.
I always do my best and, if I cheat, I learn from my mistake.

To kick the sugar habit:
It's easy to kick the sugar habit.
I don't care for the taste of sugar.
I like to change my tastes.
I like to feel good.

To maintain your weight:
I like to eat well each and every day — I feel so good.
I like myself more each and every day — I live life to the hilt.
I'm thin — I like to be happy.

To believe in success:
Each day I discover my self-worth.
I like my qualities — I'm worth something.
I have the right to succeed — I deserve to succeed.
I was born to succeed and I am succeeding.

A word of caution: while repeating these sentences, you may say to yourself: "This is ridiculous — who am I trying to kid?" What you must realize, however, is that you cannot attain your goal in real life unless you've already attained it in your mind. If you don't believe in these techniques to program your subconscious for success, don't practice them. Unless you have faith, the suggestions won't reach your subconscious.

Practice one suggestion at a time, never more, and repeat it once a day for at least 21 days. Once your goal has been reached, you can move on to another suggestion.

I have put together on cassette a series of 20 programs, each preceded by a technique to induce relaxation. The exercises last about six minutes each and may be repeated one or several times a day, as required.

Here is the list of programs contained on the cassette *Be Thin by Suggestion*:

1- Short relaxation technique
2- Program for losing weight.
3- Program to take one day at a time.
4- Program to eliminate guilt.
5- Program to eliminate feelings of food deprivation.
6- Program to eliminate the taste for sugar.
7- Program to eliminate the taste for fat.
8- Program to eliminate the influence of the surroundings.
9- Program to control your emotions.
10- Program to demystify food.
11- Program to learn to reward oneself.
12- Program to get 100% involved.
13- Program for physical activity.
14- Program for weight maintenance.
15- Program to eliminate nibbling.
16- Program to stop smoking.
17- Program to stop drinking.
18- Program to develop love of oneself and of others.
19- Program to develop self-confidence.

20- Program to believe in success.

These programs have proven highly effective. I suggest you make up a program of your own suited to your particular needs based on the relaxation and suggestion techniques I've described. Even when you're not in the alpha state, you can benefit from autosuggestion by repeating to yourself as often as possible during the day some of the sentences you've composed to program yourself. It's an excellent way to complement your deep-relaxation programming and can even replace it if you haven't got the time to induce the alpha state.

The power of words

Scientists are in the process of developing a computer that can be programmed by the human voice. By the year 2000, we'll be able to program our home computer by simply talking to it. This activity should be familiar to us, because we've been programming our subconscious with words since birth. Everything we say, especially everything we say to ourselves, is recorded in our brain; this information then serves as the basis for our self-image.

It's been estimated that we speak to ourselves at a rate of 1,200 words a minute. These words are digested by the brain just as the food we eat is digested by the stomach. And, just as the body is affected by what we eat, so the brain is affected by what we say. We've already seen that our subconscious works like a computer which compiles and stores the information it receives. If we program our subconscious negatively, we can get only negative results. The words we use are therefore of the utmost importance, for they're absorbed by our subconscious and have a direct effect on our self-image.

Here are eight indispensable programming techniques to help you on the road to success.

1- *The STOP technique*

Whenever you catch yourself saying negative things about yourself, for example: "I can't do it," "I'll never make it," "I'm hopeless," "It's always my fault," "Life is unfair," "I'm worthless," "I'm pitiful," "I can't help it — that's the way I am," say out loud: "Stop!" and visualize a stop sign. Then picture yourself as you'd like to be — as if you'd already reached the goal you've set for yourself. If you're not yet able to conjure up such a scene, try to imagine yourself in a pleasant situation.

Don't worry if at the beginning your negative thoughts recur frequently; they're often the result of many years of negative programming. Just use the STOP technique as often as necessary. After a few days, you'll notice that you employ the technique automatically as soon as a negative thought pops into your head. It won't be long before your negative thoughts become less and less frequent. The STOP technique works wonders — use it as required.

2- *To remotivate yourself*

Have you ever wondered why, when faced with a difficult situation, you occasionally lose your motivation? Often, it's because you're tormented by contradictory thoughts — you're literally fighting with yourself. For example, when someone offers you a piece of cake at a party, you may say to yourself: "Everyone's eating, so why can't I? Why should I deprive myself? No, I'd better not have any — I'll hate myself afterwards. But why can't I be like everyone else? Maybe if I had just a small piece? No, I don't think I should — I won't be able to stop myself and I'll end up gaining two pounds. Oh, what the heck, we only have one life to live, and after all, it is a party. I deserve to eat cake as much as anyone else . . ."

The reason you sometimes lose your motivation after such an inner debate is because you don't ask yourself the right questions. Your arguments are false and have nothing to do with reality. Try asking yourself these questions instead: "Why should I eat cake just because everyone else is? Most of the people eating cake are obese — are they good examples to follow? If everyone were taking drugs, would I feel obliged to copy them? All right, so they want to destroy themselves — is that any reason for me to do likewise? Does refusing to eat cake when I'd rather not really make me different from others? Wouldn't being obese make me different? What would I rather deprive myself of, a piece of cake or my health, my youth, my energy, my appearance, and my personal satisfaction? What's more important to me, a slice of cake or my self-respect?"

To help yourself ask the right questions, try the following: find a photo of yourself at your fattest and write on the back all the disadvantages of weighing so much. Don't hold anything back, and be as specific as possible. Should you lack space, continue on a separate sheet of paper and staple it to the photo. Then find another photo of yourself, this time at your ideal weight. If you don't have such a photo, try to obtain a picture of someone else who is at his or her ideal weight and who has approximately the same height and build as you and replace this person's head in the picture with your own. Be realistic in your choice of a model. Now, jot down on the back of the picture all the advantages of being at your ideal weight.

The next time you're faced with a difficult situation, say, when you're offered a piece of cake at a party, take out the two photos and place the "overweight" one on the left and the "ideal weight" one on the right. Then, ask yourself the right questions: "If I eat this cake, I'll end up looking like the picture on the left and suffer all the disadvantages of being overweight; if I don't eat any, I'll resemble the picture on the right and enjoy all the advantages of being at my ideal weight. Now, what shall I do?"

If you opt for the left and stray from your goal temporarily, as you're entitled to, you must then accept the consequences if you put on weight, without feeling guilty. You're allowed to take a small detour before getting back on track. You can even quit if you want. But make sure you ask yourself the right questions. When you know everything you have to lose and everything you have to gain, the choice is an easy one.

3- *To develop self-confidence*

Nobody is born with self-confidence — it must be acquired. If you've never been successful before in a particular activity, you have no way of knowing if you can do it and you'll lack self-confidence. On the other hand, if you've already succeeded at something once or twice, you'll be confident in your ability to do it again and you'll succeed with ease.

A hundred pounds is a lot of weight to lose. Would you feel confident about losing that much weight if you had to? I once had a patient who, before she came to see me, had already lost 100 pounds six times. When I asked her if she thought she could do it again, she told me she'd have no trouble at all, because she'd already done it in the past. However, when I asked her if she'd be able to maintain her weight once she lost her excess pounds, she began fidgeting and looked ill at ease. She had no confidence in her ability to remain at her ideal weight, having never done it before. Other patients of mine have a great deal of difficulty losing weight after a pregnancy or other special situation, but are very confident about maintaining their weight once they've shed their extra pounds. Why? Because they've already done it before.

Self-confidence is built upon memories of past successes. All of us have experienced at least one success in our lives. Unfortunately, we rarely give ourselves the credit we deserve; when we accomplish something, we take it for granted.

All the little things you do well in your daily life, be it on the job, during your leisure hours, or in your interpersonal relationships, should be interpreted as successes. It's not only the major accomplishments that count. By chalking up small victories day after day, week after week, you'll develop the habit of success and build up your self-confidence. Losing six pounds in a month is a victory, just as refusing a piece of cake or doing 10 sit-ups are. Each evening, sit down for a moment and think about all the good things you've accomplished that day. You should also go back in memory every so often and relive all your successful experiences, big and small. The more detailed you can make them, the better. What's most important is that you recapture the *feeling* of success, for the more successful you feel, the more successful you'll be. Success breeds success.

As for your past failures, try to reevaluate those that have affected you the most and eliminate all the related negative feelings. Your past mistakes were not catastrophic — you have the right to make them and have no reason to feel guilty or to suffer ego damage because of them. Instead of blaming yourself needlessly for your errors, look upon them as golden opportunities to improve yourself. The more mistakes you make, the more chances you have to learn about yourself. Mistakes are the stepping stones to success.

Each time you fail or run into difficulties, ask yourself — out loud is best — "What can I get out of this experience? What's the positive side?" At first, you may not see anything positive about what's happened to you, but every cloud has a silver lining. Once you start learning from your mistakes to improve yourself, you'll be filled with a sense of pride and accomplishment. You'll feel you're in control of your life — you'll know that nothing can stop you from succeeding.

4- *Love yourself to love others*

If you don't love yourself, how can you love others or expect others to love you? You can't give something you don't have. Interestingly, the more you love yourself, the more you'll love others; the happier you are, the more you'll make those around you happy.

Selfishness is a characteristic of someone who has so little love inside that he's afraid of losing what he has; he doesn't dare give to others. In general, such a person thinks only of himself and is very distrustful.

Loving yourself is something that must be learned. Think of all your good qualities — physical, intellectual, and moral — and write them down on a piece of paper. Ask your friends and loved ones to help you, and don't belittle the appreciation these people have for you by thinking they're merely trying to please you. Then read the list out loud several times a day. Don't forget that the greatest quality a person can have is to be open to change — to want to acquire the qualities he's lacking. To love yourself, you must accept yourself as you are with your good points and bad, but you must also work at improving yourself. You've already made a list of all your good qualities; now make one of all your faults and try to think of how you can better yourself.

If you believe you have more weakensses than strengths, you're either underestimating yourself or you're suffering from nervous depression. In both cases, you'd best consult a psychotherapist or a physician. We all possess far more good qualities than bad; unfortunately, we don't always appreciate our virtues.

You can't solve your weight problem unless you learn to truly love yourself. Repeat every day: "I'm the most important person in my life."

5- *Avoid the negative*

Everything you say about yourself, and everything others say about you, has a direct bearing on how you think and behave. When psychologists interviewed inmates at a prison, they found that 80 percent of them had turned out exactly as others said they would. Their parents had always told them: "You're good for nothing — you'll end up in prison." The influence of others can also be positive. I recently heard a professional baseball player say that he wasn't surprised by his success in the National League because his parents never stopped encouraging him from the time he was eight years old. "You'll make it to the major leagues," they kept telling him. "You'll be a fine pitcher one day."

Hearing something once, though, is not enough. A message must be repeated many times for its effect to be felt. That's why advertisements are run over and over again. If they're repeated often enough, we end up believing them.

In Chapter 2, we saw how the influences of society program us negatively. Since our brain makes no distinction between what's good for us and what's not, it's very important to avoid negative influences — they're poison.

Stay away from negative people. There are those who will tell you it's not worth losing weight because you'll gain it back; others will say they know someone who became sick as a result of dieting; still others will try to persuade you that dieting is making you look older.

There's no use arguing with such people — they're so negative, it's impossible to change them. You can try to understand their behavior and sympathize with them in your mind, but don't let them sway you. You mustn't let anyone or anything stop you from attaining your goals.

Negative news, be it in the newspaper, on television, or on the radio, should also be avoided. How can you maintain a positive, healthy outlook on life if all you read and hear about is tragedy? One of my regular patients, a 55-year-old pharmacist, is usually very cheerful. On his last visit, however, he looked totally depressed. "Nothing's going right," he moaned. "The whole world's a mess." Surprised by his negative attitude, I asked him if he'd lost his job.

"No," he replied, "everything's fine at work."

"Are you having problems at home? Is somebody ill?"

"No, the wife and kids are very well, and so am I."

"Are you or your children having financial problems?"

"No, I have a 33-year-old son who's an engineer and a 29-year-old daughter who's a pharmacist. They're both doing fine."

"May I ask, then, why you seem so unhappy this morning?"

"Don't you read the papers, Dr. Larocque? Don't you watch the news on T.V.?"

Here's a man who has everything he needs to be happy, yet he doesn't appreciate it. Instead, he lets himself be influenced by all the negative news in the media.

Don't let the merchants of doom get to you. Try as much as possible to surround yourself with positive people and to live in a positive atmosphere.

6- *To maintain your enthusiasm*

It's 8 o'clock in the morning. The telephone wakes you up. At the other end of the line, a friend of yours says: "I thought I'd call you up this morning to tell you how wonderful I think you are. I feel so full of enthusiasm this morning, and it's all because of you. You're a model to me and a source of inspiration. You're the most important person I know. Have a nice day!"

If a friend called you one morning and said those words to you, how would you feel? You'd probably be filled with enthusiasm, wouldn't you? I know I would. To be appreciated by a friend is a wonderful feeling — your self-esteem can't help but grow. So what are you waiting for? You are your best friend. Each morning when you wake up, give yourself a call and repeat those inspiring words to yourself.

Enthusiasm is the key ingredient in the recipe for success. We weren't born enthusiastic, we were born crying. Enthusiasm is something that must be acquired; once acquired, it must be nurtured, like a flower that must be watered every day. I hope this book has filled you with enthusiasm, but unless you cultivate it, your enthusiasm will soon die.

Each morning upon awakening, leap joyfully out of bed and say to yourself: "It's great to be alive! I'm going to succeed — I can just feel it." Keep thinking enthusiastically throughout the day. Repeat to yourself: "I like myself. I'm proud of myself. I'm pleased with my efforts to improve myself." By repeating positive things about yourself as often as possible, you'll become more and more enthusiastic. In less than three weeks, you'll notice that your behavior has started to change. You may even be surprised by your enthusiastic attitude and try to find explanations for it. Don't worry, it's for real. Just keep thinking positively, and the world will be your oyster. You are what you think.

Another way of maintaining your enthusiasm is to spend a few minutes a day reading inspiring passages from books on motivation and positive thinking. The secret of this technique is to read the passages that interest you not once or twice, but over and over and over again, so the message really sinks in. Read your favorite paragraph or page five times, ten times, twenty times, until it becomes embedded in your subconscious. This way, your enthusiasm will never wane. You are what you think.

A similar technique which I find particularly useful for maintaining an enthusiastic attitude is to listen to cassettes on motivation. When you read a book, you hear your own voice and your own intonations, which may not necessarily communicate the same enthusiasm as that of the person who wrote the work. However, when you listen to a cassette on motivation, the person you hear will probably be bubbling with enthusiasm, which will make the message all the more effective.

Another advantage of cassettes is that they can be listened to any time, any place. You can play them while doing the housework, while cooking, while taking a walk, while lying on the beach, or while driving your car. I also recommend that you use headphones (except when driving), because they surround you with the words and sounds and make an even greater impression on your subconscious. A number of my patients have been using my *Be Thin, Be Motivated* cassettes for several months now with excellent results.

It's not easy to maintain a high level of enthusiasm in our society, because we're surrounded by negative influences. If you look around you, you'll see that most people are negative and apathetic. To counteract the daily bombardment of negative messages, we need something positive that we can hear as often as possible. Repetition is the key. For every ten negative messages we hear, we need ten positive. We are what we think. Even if you're highly enthusiastic right now, if you stop thinking positively and putting positive things in your life, in a few days the negative will regain the upper hand. The opposite is also true: even if you're very negative now, if you start thinking positively and surround yourself with positive things and positive people, in a few days the positive will win out over the negative.

Summary

You are now on the road to success. You have everything you need to succeed. You know that you are what you think, and that success breeds success. By using your imagination, you can dream of attaining the goals you've set for yourself. It's your duty to make the most of everything God gave you.

By inducing the alpha state and using the power of suggestion, you can build up your confidence and self-esteem. By using the power of words, you can say STOP to negative thoughts and stay motivated by asking yourself the right questions. You can develop your self-confidence by making a point of remembering your past successes and reinterpreting your failures. You can learn to love yourself and accept yourself as you are, with your good points and bad, and thereby learn to love others more as well. You can learn to avoid negative influences, and to maintain your enthusiasm by repetition.

The techniques presented in this book will work only if you believe in them. If you don't have faith, forget it — you're just wasting your time. For the techniques to be effective, you must also eliminate the mental blocks that have been preventing you from programming yourself positively. Finally, you must make a point of practicing and repeating the techniques every day, without fail. Then you'll be on the road to success.

CHAPTER 22

THE BEGINNING

The book you've just read is unlike any other. It's a new, effective tool to help you solve your weight problem once and for all so you can enjoy a happy and exciting life.

Reading it will mark the beginning of your development as a person, a development which will enable you to shed your excess weight with ease. It will mark the beginning of a new way of thinking which will help you turn your dreams into reality. It will mark the beginning of a life of true happiness.

This book is like your potential: it has no ending, no limit — only a beginning. Re-read it often. You'll be surprised at how many new insights you'll have at each reading — ideas that may have escaped you at first.

This book is like a bottomless well: it can continually inspire and motivate you. It marks the beginning of a new life for you.